THE BIG
DOME

The Dome Mine headframe at sunset.

Photo by Eric Peterson

THE BIG DOME

OVER SEVENTY YEARS OF GOLD MINING IN CANADA

BY
CHARLES P. GIRDWOOD,
LAWRENCE F. JONES
AND GEORGE LONN

CYBERGRAPHICS COMPANY INCORPORATED, TORONTO, CANADA

This book is dedicated to the memory of
Clifford W. Michel
President, 1943-1958; Chairman, 1959-1976

*Specimens of exceptionally
high-grade gold ore:
From the Dome Mine (top)
From the Sigma Mine (centre)
From the Campbell Red Lake
Mine (below)*

CONTENTS

Part of northern and southern
Ontario showing locations of
Dome Group properties

FOREWORD

The story of "The Big Dome" is one of the classics of hardrock mining in the Canadian shield. Dome was the first among the large Canadian gold mines to be discovered and today, after seventy-four years of continuous operation, is the only one which could be classified as a major producer of gold.

From the exciting first surface showing in the Porcupine area of northern Ontario, the Dome Mines group of companies has grown to become the largest gold producer in Canada, accounting for over 20 per cent of the country's annual production. The original mine, "The Big Dome" has demonstrated a unique durability and still has a potential life of many years.

No one associated with Dome can fail to appreciate that this is a story of people. Over four generations have contributed to Dome's achievements and deserve our gratitude for its success. It is to them - the miners, geologists, engineers, maintenance staff, mill and office personnel and mine managers - that this history pays tribute. During its formative years and through the extremely difficult periods of depression and war, their sheer human effort and determination kept the property in production.

It is hoped that this volume will not only be known as a Company history of note providing a glimpse of the early days of mining in our country, but will inspire and encourage yet further development of Canadian mineral resources. We also hope it will enhance confidence and pride in the Canadian mining industry.

In 1978, several photograph albums depicting the early years of Dome Mines were received from Mrs. A.S. Tatum, daughter of a former manager of the mine, the late H.P. DePencier. These records stimulated a search for other historical information and it soon became apparent that Dome had a unique story which deserved to be told.

Unfortunately, parts of the story are incomplete. A great deal of material has been lost over the years, but the amount of information still available was surprising and encouraging. Much of this comes from the recollections of the few remaining employees from the early years at Dome. It is to be hoped that this account will bring to light additional items of historical value.

Charles P. Girdwood, a former Vice-President and General Manager, undertook the task of guiding production of this book. He was fortunate in having available the services of George Lonn, Lawrence F. Jones and Roy Longo, who did much of the research, writing and editing respectively. Their task was facilitated by the assistance of a number of good friends of Dome Mines. For their recollections, special thanks go to James B. Redpath, Mrs. J.G.L. (Queenie) McCrea, Kenneth B. Dowsett, Dr. William F. James, Edmund J. Andrecheck and Bryce Mackenzie. Gratitude is also expressed to Clifford L. Michel, Miss Adele C. Pighi and James Alexander for the details provided concerning the career of Clifford W. Michel.

Assistance was also received from L. Carson Brown, retired information officer in the Mines Division, Ontario Ministry of Natural Resources and from the staffs of other governmental agencies and industry associations. The kind cooperation of Dr. Walter Curlook, President of Inco Metals Limited, made it possible to obtain information which would otherwise have been unavailable.

The colour photographs used with the text, especially those contributed by George Hunter, Eric Peterson, George Lonn and Paul Gelinas, have greatly enhanced the graphic quality of the book. In addition, we are grateful to Michael S. Farrell of the United Steelworkers of America for his help in obtaining some of the early photographs.

Mr. Robin Brass was engaged as a consulting editor and his many helpful suggestions were much appreciated, as were the contributions of William McLean and assistance given by Monica Hanula and Jill Richardson.

The preparation of a history of this sort involves the assistance and cooperation of many more people than we are able to name here. We offer our apologies to any person or organization who assisted but for reasons of space must be omitted from these acknowledgements. To them and to all who helped make "The Big Dome" possible, we extend our warmest thanks.

A.B. Matthews
Chairman

M.A. Taschereau
President

March, 1983

CHAPTER 1

Before the Days
of the Dome

Most of Ontario and nearly all of Quebec lie in the great Canadian Shield, a massive horseshoe of Precambrian rock which surrounds Hudson and James Bays and spans the greater part of the eastern half of Canada. Born of cataclysmic convulsions of the earth after it had solidified from a molten mass, the Shield dates back at least 2½ billion years, preceding the Cambrian era 600 million years ago which saw the first appearance of life, traced by the presence of fossils in rock formations. Contractions of the earth's crust, subterranean upheavals, and long ages of glacial advances and retreats have battered and scarred the Shield, wearing away the younger surface rocks and exposing the ancient layers beneath.

A thick blanket of forest was slowly built up over many thousands of years, covering the harsh, exposed rocks with a protective layer of dense, green and fragrant timber. It was not until yesterday, relatively speaking in geological time, that wildlife began to make its appearance: deer, moose, bear, beaver and many smaller species soon filled the bush, providing food and clothing for the first humans in North America, the Indians. This existence was to change dramatically with the coming of the European white man.

For 250 years, explorers, voyageurs and fur traders paddled the lakes and rivers that laced the densely forested rocky wilderness of northern Ontario. The heavy boot of a portaging traveller may have scuffed away moss from an outcropping of rock, unwittingly exposing a vein of quartz and a glimmer of gold. This lay unnoticed, however, until the first decade of the twentieth century, when the region emerged as one of the world's great mining centres.

Between the years 1845 and 1900, much prospecting had been carried out in other parts of Ontario, with the result that copper was found west of Sudbury in the Bruce Peninsula area, gold and silver near Madoc and in the Lake of the Woods vicinity, and silver on Silver Islet in Lake Superior.

Except for the discovery in 1883 and subsequent development of nickel-copper mines in the Sudbury region, the search for minerals in Ontario gave little return to pioneering prospectors. For example, the Silver Islet mine commenced production in 1868 and, over the next sixteen years, produced silver to the value of about $3.5 million before the fierce Lake Superior storms proved too powerful to allow continued production. Most of the mines in eastern Ontario and the Bruce Mines copper properties amounted to little, and near the Lake of the Woods, promising surface showings eventually petered out, taking the expected boom in the gold mining industry with them. Many geologists, basing their beliefs on past disappointments, insisted that it was simply not possible to find gold in economic quantities in the province.

Fortunately, not all geologists held the same pessimistic view. In 1896, nearly ten years before the exciting events that would transform the Porcupine district of northern Ontario from a wilderness into a miner's paradise, Dr. W. A. Parks, of the University of Toronto, came upon a gold-bearing quartz vein during a geological investigation in the southwestern corner of Whitney Township, an area in which there would later be seven producing mines. Dr. Parks wrote: "I regard the region south of the trail to Porcupine Lake as giving promise of rich reward to the prospector."

That same year, Edward M. Burwash, a geologist with the fledgling Ontario Bureau of Mines, spent some time in Shaw Township, a few miles south of what later became the Porcupine mining camp. In his *Geology of the Nipissing-Algoma Line*, Burwash wrote:

> On the first half of the 116th line a small quartz vein occurs which, on assay, was found to contain a trace of gold. From the 120th mile the Redstone River (Neminisibe) runs eastward to Night Hawk Lake. The shores of the river and lake are occupied by banks of clay, but the underlying rocks wherever exposed appear to be Huronian. The district would be a promising one from a prospector's point of view were it not for the presence of drift (rock debris).

Burwash cautiously qualified his statements: a *small* quartz vein, a *trace* of gold, a *promising* (district) *were it not for*. But GOLD, the key word, was there for every venturesome prospector to act upon.

Another early explorer who virtually stumbled on the Porcupine was a brilliant young geologist named Charles Camsell. Employed by the Algoma Central Railway of Sault Ste. Marie, he was sent north to prospect for iron ore deposits.

Returning late in the fall of 1901 by way of the Hudson Bay Company route through the Porcupine, from the Abitibi River west to the Mattagami River, he noticed outcroppings of quartz on the portage between what were later known as Pearl Lake and Miller Lake. Liking the look of the rocks and the general geology, he knocked off several specimens for assay back in Sault Ste. Marie.

The samples assayed $5.20 in gold to the ton, or better than a quarter-ounce to the ton, rich by today's standards. In those days, however, the amount was not worth considering and the discovery was not followed up.

The extension of the railway into the more distant northland of Ontario unintentionally sparked a revival of prospecting in the early 1900s. Anxious to open up the 330,000 square-mile area of "New Ontario," ten government exploration parties were dispatched in 1899 to carry out a two-year study. On their return, they reported enthusiastically on the region's wealth in natural resources: land sufficiently fertile to offset the disadvantages of a short growing season, limitless stocks of timber, forests filled with game, lakes and streams teeming with fish, and rivers with the potential of conversion into hydro-electric power. Minerals were also mentioned as resources that could be exploited. In response to these glowing accounts, the government of Ontario built a railway from North Bay northwards to the Haileybury-New Liskeard area, thus opening up the clay belt west of Lake Temiskaming to settlers and providing a link to the southern markets for the lumber trade. This line, known for many years as the Temiskaming and Northern Ontario (T. & N.O.) Railway, was eventually renamed the Ontario Northland Railway. Although originally intended for farmers and timbermen, the T. & N.O. proved to be a godsend for prospectors, who had previously confined their work to areas south of the Canadian Pacific Railway. Mining operations had usually been limited to accessible locations fairly close to the Great Lakes or to a railway. Now, at last, a ribbon of steel wound its way through the northern wilderness, and prospectors could find their way to their own Eldorados.

By the summer of 1903, the railway had reached the north end of Long Lake, five miles from the town of Haileybury on Lake Temiskaming. A silver discovery there led to the first "rush" in Ontario's history, and the first in Canada since the days of the Klondike. There are two versions of this discovery, one being the story of Fred LaRose of Hull, Quebec, a blacksmith working on the construction of the railway. Angrily hurling his hammer at a fox skulking nearby, it is said, he missed and the hammer smashed instead into an outcrop of rock, exposing native silver. The other version concerns J.H. McKinley and his partner, E.J. Darragh, suppliers of ties for the railway, who uncovered thin metallic samples from the vicinity of Long Lake, and sent them to McGill University for assaying. They turned out to be silver.

As a sidelight, after Fred LaRose made his unusual find, Noah and Henry Timmins of Mattawa (of later Hollinger mine fame) purchased a one-quarter interest in his holdings for $3,500, and were also given the option to purchase an additional quarter for $25,000. After deciding to take up this offer, the brothers were left strapped for cash, so they approached a bank in Haileybury for a $5,000 loan. Even after offering two freight cars loaded with silver ore as collateral, estimated by Dr. Willet G. Miller, the Provincial Geologist, to be worth at least $30,000, the bank manager abruptly refused their request.

Fuming, Noah scraped together enough money to head for New York, returning a few weeks later with a cheque for $50,000, drawn on the Guggenheim account. The bank manager, after being handed the cheque, spluttered that he couldn't cash it as there weren't enough funds in the bank. Plucking the slip of paper from the manager's trembling hands, Timmins coldly told him that he was only to look at it, not to cash it. "This," he said triumphantly, "is the security I offered you for a $5,000 loan. I won't be bothering you further — we have arranged for another bank to start up in this country and they have no objections to handling mining accounts." With that parting shot, Noah stalked out, head held high.

Dr. Miller marked the site of the discovery with a hand-lettered sign that proclaimed: "THIS IS COBALT," so named because of the marked presence of cobalt minerals in the area. By 1905, Cobalt was much more than a flag station on the shining new rails of the T. & N.O. A community of tents, log shacks and lean-tos, with deeply rutted roads that passed for streets, it was a lodestar that drew fortune hunters from every part of Canada, the United States, and the British Isles. A new interest in prospecting developed as tales of sudden mineral wealth swept across the north. Men gave up their jobs on farms or in the logging camps or shops to devote their time to the frantic search for mineral wealth. Others, more conservative in their ways, became part-time prospectors.

A broad description of prospectors was given in the *Souvenir Booklet Celebrating the Golden Anniversary of the Porcupine Gold Rush*, published in 1959:

> The early prospectors did more than just prospect. They took active part in the general progress and development of the district. They blazed trails into the new camp, and helped bring in supplies and equipment. If there were any pressing need — for transportation, stopping places, boat services, or anything else, the prospectors would see that the need was filled.

The search for buried treasure spread as prospectors picked up enticing tales that gold had been found in the wilderness of Porcupine. The T. & N.O. now extended to Cochrane, where it connected with the new Transcontinental Railway. Only 100 miles on the rails brought prospectors from Cobalt to Driftwood, near the present town of Monteith, a favourite jumping-off point for those who wanted to try their luck in the Porcupine country, about 15 miles to the west.

This rush resulted in the establishment of three of the most famous gold mines in the western hemisphere: Dome, Hollinger, and McIntyre. Before this, however, there were four or five years of uncertainty and frustration, and of finds that glowed but briefly.

These early years of Porcupine's development were scantily recorded, but the first mining claim staked was attributed to Edward Orr Taylor. Aside from its recording in May 1905, nothing more was heard about his property, which lay on the southwest shore of Night Hawk Lake.

Assessment work was done in Tisdale Township by a group of prospectors led by Reuben D'Aigle an Acadian from Chipman, New Brunswick. D'Aigle, a successful placer miner in the Yukon and Alaska, moved east when he heard about Cobalt, but by the time he arrived it was too late for the action he wanted, so he headed for the Porcupine country.

D'Aigle, Bob Mustard, William Moore, and two companions dug a test pit with a hand drill and gunpowder. D'Aigle panned the broken rock for gold and found it barren. After fruitlessly cutting trails and digging trenches at various locations, the party abandoned the entire operation, even leaving behind some of their equipment. D'Aigle accepted the assertion of his partner Bob Mustard without question, that "quartz veins in Ontario just never pay to work." One of the trails was later found to have been cut right over a rich showing of gold, hidden under moss, which was staked in the summer of 1909 by Benny Hollinger and his comrades. This became the celebrated Hollinger Mine, immediate neighbour of Dome.

The first actual discovery of gold in the Porcupine district was made by two Finns, Victor Nansen and Harry Bennella, who staked claims on Gold Island in Night Hawk Lake in 1907. A shaft was sunk but the property failed to yield the continuity of values needed to survive.

During this time, Charles Auer staked claims on a peninsula that projected into Night Hawk Lake from the north shore. Over a 20-year period, the Night Hawk Peninsula Mine produced gold valued at half a million dollars.

In 1908, a year before the sensational discoveries of Jack Wilson, Harry Preston, Benny Hollinger, Sandy McIntyre and their fellow prospectors, A.G. Hunter, who had left his Toronto home to seek his fortune in the north, found a gold-bearing vein at the northeast end of Porcupine Lake. Hunter opened a mine there which operated intermittently over the next five years.

Exciting as they were, these events were insignificant compared to those of 1909. They were, in fact, but a prelude to the real drama.

CHAPTER 2

"The Big Dome," They Called it

Canada's longest-producing gold mining company was born in the summer of 1909 with the discovery of a dome of quartz with prolific showings of free gold. Whether the find was the result of a team effort directed by John S. Wilson or whether Harry Preston, one of the team members, deserves most of the credit is a clouded issue.

Clary Dixon, a veteran prospector, is quoted at length on the subject of Wilson and Preston in *Free Gold*, by H. Arnold Hoffman, published in New York in 1947. Wilson himself narrated the events of 1909 to the annual meeting of the Canadian Institute of Mining and Metallurgy, held in Quebec twenty-five years later, and his version would appear to be more plausible.

John S. (Jack) Wilson was born in 1872 in Toronto. His father, John Swinton Wilson, was a railway construction engineer whose family moved frequently because of his work. Presumably the Wilsons spent several years in the United States because Jack, at the age of 26, enlisted in Teddy Roosevelt's Rough Riders who made the famous charge up San Juan Hill in Cuba during the Spanish-American War of 1898.

Wilson returned to Canada to settle in Massey, a small town on the Canadian Pacific Railway line 60 miles west of Sudbury. Although Jack, like his father, was in the railway construction business, he soon developed a keen interest in prospecting, especially after his father-in-law, John Campbell, had joined the Cobalt silver rush. He described his first venture into the Porcupine country as follows:

> In the summer of 1907 I got word of spectacular gold having been found on Night Hawk Lake. I immediately left Massey and managed to get in with the second crew hitting the lake. The gold had been found on Gold Island – a very small island – and we could find no more visible gold in the pit from which quite a quantity of spectacular ore had been taken. We staked most of the peninsula which afterwards became the

Night Hawk Gold Mine. (Doubtless Wilson was referring to
Charles Auer's Night Hawk Peninsula Mine.)

During a few hours' delay at Englehart while en route to Night Hawk Lake by train, he passed the time riding on a handcar with a railway construction foreman. At Boston Creek, he jumped off to view some rock formations. "I brought out some quartz," he said, "which was, I think, the first sample ever taken out of the Boston Creek area. The assay afterwards showed $3.45. I tried several times to interest people in this, but was unsuccessful."

Unfortunately, the results from the Night Hawk property were not encouraging and Wilson was forced to abandon prospecting for a time. He took a job as superintendent of stores and supplies for the T. & N.O. for the construction work between the Watabeag River and Cochrane, and was based at Driftwood. But even when he fell seriously ill, he could not suppress his zest for prospecting:

In the fall of 1908 I contracted typhoid fever and became
dangerously ill. It so happened that a doctor from Thornhill,
Ontario, was interested in a company which had the contract
for building some of the bridges on the railroad. He happened
to come to Driftwood during my illness, became interested in
me, and, with permission of the company doctor, took charge
of my case. In our conversation I happened to tell him that I
was a prospector. He made me an offer to take charge of a
prospecting outfit and agreed to furnish the necessary money
for a six months' trip. I told him I had decided to operate from
the headwaters of the Porcupine River.

Early in the winter I bought two dog teams and equipment and
began to forward equipment and supplies to the shore of Frederick House Lake. I had invested quite a sum of my own money
up to this point and I wrote to the doctor, telling him to get his
organization together and have the amount of money agreed
upon deposited in the bank.

As with many prospecting ventures of the time, that one came to nought and Wilson, his zeal somewhat dampened, put it briefly and bluntly: "This organization fell through." But he was not about to give up yet.

While living in Massey, Jack Wilson met and had some "mining dealings" with W. S. "Pop" Edwards, owner of a plumbing business in Chicago, who frequently visited Ontario to fish. He now turned to his acquaintance for help, writing a letter to Edwards in which he "explained the situation and contract" and received a telegram in reply which read, "We (possibly referring to Dr. T. N. Jamieson, Edwards' partner in the grubstaking) accept contract and will

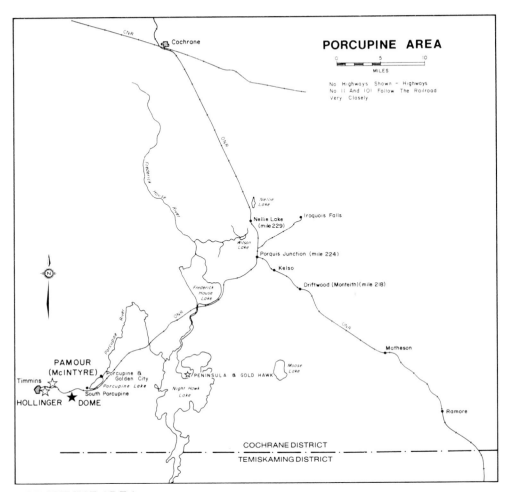

PORCUPINE AREA
Map showing communities
along the Temiskaming &
Northern Ontario Railway
(later the Ontario Northland
Railway), in the early days.

furnish capital. Cheque in mail. Come to Chicago soon as possible to sign up." According to Clary Dixon, the cheque was for $1,000, with which he bought canoes and supplies and hauled all the equipment required for his expedition to Frederick House Lake. After completing the deal with Edwards and Jamieson in Chicago, Wilson now faced the problem of transporting the equipment:

> On May 18, 1909, I took three canoes by train to Mileage 228 on the T. & N.O. and then portaged to Nellie Lake. The route then was to cross Nellie Lake to Wilson Creek, down Wilson Creek to Frederick House River, down Frederick House River to Frederick House Lake. The river and the shore were open, but the ice hadn't moved out of the balance of the lake. On May 21 the ice moved out and we followed it down the Frederick House River to Night Hawk Lake. We landed at the Charlie Auer camp, unloaded, and went back for another load. We had an outfit that weighed 4,000 pounds — we were carrying steel, a small anvil, dynamite, and coal. We arranged with Mr. Auer to cache half our outfit with him, and hired three Indians — Tom Fox, Joe Buffalo and his son. In five canoes we started across the lake in a severe storm, heading for the mouth of the Porcupine River. We had to make two trips across the lake with the load we intended to take. We reached Porcupine Lake on May 23 and made camp on the point, now known as Graveyard Point.

> Just north of our camp, a quarter of a mile along the shore, I discovered that some work had been done and was surprised to find free gold in a vein that was mostly under water. On the top of a hill we found an old, rotted tent that had evidently been left there the year before. This was the Hunter claim, afterwards known as Porcupine Lake Mining Co.

Then began the work that was to lead, about two weeks later, to the Dome discovery.

> We started in on Lot 10, Concession 2, Whitney Township. I figured I might be able to pick up the continuation of the Hunter vein, as the formation was very narrow on Hunter's claims and the strike of the vein pointed towards the ground, which we started to prospect. I had four men with me: George Burns, Frank Campbell, Cliff Campbell, and Harry Preston. We started on the north boundary of Lot 10 and ran two outside lines and two centre lines, 125 paces apart, over every 40-acre lot, keeping track of the pacings, and the location and

strike of every contact or change of formation. These 40-acre maps were built into a field map every night. We mapped everything three lots east and south to the south boundary of Whitney Township.

In this area we staked a big sulphide vein, which was afterwards called Mammoth Mines Limited.

Then, as now, staking a claim involved marking the corners of a 40-acre square of ground (1,320 feet on each side) with usually hewn squared timber posts, which stated the staker's name, his mining license number, the date, and the time staked, and subsequently registering the claim at the office of the Mining Recorder in the mining district concerned. The staker then had the exclusive right to explore and develop the mineral resources on his claim, or group of claims, and could sell this right if he wished or bring in partners to help finance his project. The right expired if a certain amount of assessment work, intended to obtain knowledge of sub-surface conditions, was not carried out on the claim within a prescribed time.

During a trip to Night Hawk Lake to pick up more dynamite and supplies, Wilson and his party met Phillip Mecklenburg looking for his lost dog. Wilson had worked with Mecklenburg on the same railway job. When Mecklenburg expressed an interest in joining the group, Wilson promptly hired him as cook.

About this time another crew hit Porcupine Lake – George Bannerman and Tom Geddes, who camped on the northwest side of the lake. When they saw our fire, they came over to visit us and said they had been there the year before and had gotten some small assays and values. They agreed that if we would give them time to prospect their ground, they would let us know if they struck anything. We made the agreement mutual. About this time Cliff Campbell quit, and on my trip out to record the Mammoth properties I hired Gilbert Rheault in his place.

We then worked west and south of Porcupine Lake, prospected, and mapped all of the ground west for three lots north of the south boundary line of Tisdale Township, until we struck the formation comprising the Dome Mines. About 110 feet northeast of the mound of quartz, afterwards called the Dome, two exposures of quartz were found, one 21 feet thick, the other 12 feet wide, and about 92 feet apart. I took some samples from the 12-foot exposure and, panning, got two fine colours of gold. This was late in June. A few days later we staked four claims. When I went out to record, I had the samples run and got $7.50 in gold across 12 feet.

Before going out to record, I told two men to put a cross-cut across the 21-foot vein. On my return, they reported nothing in sight. In my absence, George Bannerman's crew on the north and west sides of Porcupine Lake had made a spectacular find. My crew had been over to see it and were very excited about it. They wanted me to go over next day and stake beside Bannerman. (This Bannerman property was later called the Scottish Ontario Gold Mines.) This I refused to do, as my assay showed good values from the first samplings. Two of the crew said they were going to quit. I told them I was moving camp at four o'clock in the morning and if they refused to go I would give them enough supplies but could not spare them a canoe. I also told them they would lose their interest in the exploration. They finally agreed to stay.

We took three canoes and loads to the south end of the lake, went up the creek that comes in at the south end of Porcupine Lake, and portaged across to our discovery. I looked at the 21-foot cross-cut. The quartz looked much more "friendly" where it was opened up. I told the crew to go back for another load of supplies and I started to examine the work.

I made a brush broom and swept the trench clean. As I was on my hands and knees examining the seams in the quartz, about 12 feet ahead of me I saw a piece of yellow glisten as the sun struck it. I crawled up to it, and it proved to be a very spectacular piece of gold sticking out of a small piece of quartz that had rolled back into the trench. It lay in a little thin seam of schist. I started looking for this seam, but couldn't find it. One large block of quartz that had been blown out lay on one side of the trench. On one of the lower corners I discovered a little black seam. I got a striking hammer and broke into this seam, and uncovered a wonderful showing of gold.

I sized up the big block of quartz, discovered where it came from, and I found the seam then crossing the cross-cut. But the schist had worked out a little of it and I found that it contained a lot of loose free gold. Working along the seam I managed to break below the honeycombed zone, and got about 10 pounds of very spectacular specimens.

When the boys came back with the second load, I showed them what I had found. We got out the drills and hammers and put in a row of holes along this seam and opened up a regular "jewel-

*Photographs of the original
quartz outcrops on the Dome
property, circa 1909–10.*

lery shop." Three of us went as far as the old camp that night with 132 pounds of very spectacular specimens. At daybreak Phil Mecklenburg and I started for the track. I left word for the boys to stop all work and stake the ground, which afterwards comprised the Dome Extension, and also added two more claims to the Dome stakings. I shipped the specimens to Mr. Edwards in Chicago and told him to come, at once — which he did. In my absence, the boys, after doing their staking, started to strip the northeast nose of the Big Dome of Quartz, and under the moss and dirt uncovered that wonderful showing which caused so much excitement.

Clary Dixon's version of the Dome discovery places more emphasis on the role played by Harry Preston. In Wilson's account, Preston was merely one of the five men who made up his prospecting party. Dixon, basing his facts on what he had heard when he visited the Dome site soon after the discovery, asserted that everyone in Wilson's team (including Wilson), except for Harry Preston, left the camp at Graveyard Point (which Dixon referred to as Deadman's Point) to investigate an exciting silver find near Sudbury. Preston stayed behind, Dixon said, because he had a hunch about the area where the Wilson crew was then working. One day, while walking alone, Preston missed his footing on a rocky knoll, scraping away some moss that covered the rock. He looked down to see a rough and jagged length of free gold — gold in its natural state which, when it was completely uncovered, measured 21 feet wide and led to a great mound or dome of quartz which, Dixon said, was "all covered with gold."

Clary Dixon also recalled an incident afterwards while camping on the shore of Porcupine Creek with Tom Middleton, a fellow prospector. The pair kept close to a raging camp fire, built to ward off a sudden evening chill, when they suddenly heard water splashing. Thinking that it might be a moose, Dixon picked up his rifle and stealthily hurried to the water's edge. "Don't shoot!" cried Middleton. "I think it's a man!" Sure enough, a canoe appeared, gliding through the rushes and reeds of the marshy shore, with Harry Preston paddling. The co-finder of the Big Dome had heard they were in the district and set out to visit them, guided by the light of their fire. Several years earlier, Preston had met the pair in the Gowganda district, where they had tipped him on moose tracks they had seen. After adding three moose to his food supply, Preston felt he "owed them one", so he mentioned that there was still a great deal of searching going on in the area, especially for what he called "white rock," or quartz. "There's plenty of it west of here, between the long lake (later Gillies Lake) and a small lake a bit to the southwest," Preston said. "Stake there and you'll have something."

After Preston had left, Middleton and Dixon bickered over what to do. Tom was eager to investigate Preston's tip, but Clary was reluctant, as they were on their way home, with just enough supplies to last, and had already used up all their prospecting licenses. Dixon won out. "I made a great mistake," Dixon said regretfully. "Those white rocks Preston was talking about were the Hollinger mine, and Benny Hollinger and Alex Gillies didn't get there until long after the time we would have found it if we had gone. We could have had the works!"

Back in Haileybury, Jack Miller, their grubstaker, was disappointed with the groups of claims they had staked. Refusing to allow them to be recorded, he rebuked them for staking claims without any signs of gold. These "unsatisfactory" claims turned out to be the sites of two profitable properties, West Dome and McIntyre. "Just a matter of a few million dollars," Clary Dixon said wryly.

When Wilson returned and saw Preston's discovery, he left at once for Chicago to give the wonderful news to Edwards in person and to seek additional funds. Preston set off a blast of dynamite in the quartz dome that exposed a shining display of gold-spattered quartz, Dome's "golden stairway," the like of which none of the prospectors had ever seen before or ever again expected to see. When he arrived with two other prospectors from Kelso soon after, Clary Dixon found Preston standing guard with a rifle.

One of the visitors described it: "The gold was in blobs, like candle drippings, and . . . in sponge-like masses, some of them as large as a cup, lying under the moss in a dome-shaped outcrop of quartz. 'The Big Dome,' they called it."

The five members of the expedition, having used up their quota of three claims per man, could not legally stake the "golden stairway," but did so anyway, hoping that Wilson would return with new licenses before invading prospectors, wise to the limits of the law, supplanted their claims. Wilson did arrive in time, and "The Big Dome" was legally staked.

It is clear that the two accounts of the Dome discovery differ substantially. Wilson, in his report to the mining association at Quebec, made no mention of Preston or anyone else having uncovered the original find; he merely said that "two exposures of quartz were found." This first vein, however, was named after Jack Wilson's wife, Ida Maud. Wilson made no mention of his visit to Sudbury or of going to Chicago to meet his grubstakers, saying instead that he had "shipped the specimens to Mr. Edwards," urging him to come to the Porcupine site at once.

Mining officials in Toronto endorsed Harry Preston as the discoverer of the Dome by accident rather than by design. In a 50th Porcupine gold-mining anniversary issue of the *Timmins Daily Press* published on June 30, 1954, the Ontario Department of Mines inserted the following advertisement:

HE STUBBED HIS TOE ON A GOLD MINE!

Harry Preston stood at the top of an embankment and gazed at the rain-drenched bushland stretching west from Porcupine Lake. Then, motioning to his two fellow prospectors to follow, he started down the steep cliff . . . stumbled . . . clutched wildly at the slippery moss . . . dug in his heels. Amid the laughter of his comrades, he turned to see how far he had fallen . . . the laughter stopped abruptly.

Where the moss had been torn away, a ledge of quartz, twenty-one feet wide, led to a dome-shaped structure studded with gold! It was just fifty years ago that Harry Preston stumbled over the world-famous Gold Dome Mine. Since then, Ontario's gold-mining industry has contributed over 2½ billion dollars of new wealth to our Province. More than half of this has come from the Porcupine Mines.

In August of 1974, the *Canadian Geographical Journal* published an article entitled "The Golden Porcupine" by L. Carson Brown, the information services officer for the Ontario Ministry of Natural Resources (Mines Division), which was later reprinted as a pamphlet by the Ministry. Supporting neither Dixon's nor Wilson's account, he wrote:

> As three members of the (prospecting) party, Jack Wilson of Massey, George Burns and Harry Preston were moving through the bush, Preston slipped on a rocky knoll and the heels of his boots stripped the moss from a wide quartz vein, displaying flecks of gold. When this was uncovered the startled prospectors found themselves gazing at a mound of glittering quartz covered with gold. Here, if the gold carried down, was a real bonanza. The Dome Mine, founded on the discovery, has given ample indication in the succeeding years that the surface promise did indeed go to considerable depth.

The true version may never be known. All of the participants in the discovery are long gone. When Jack Wilson died in Parry Sound in 1948 at the age of 76, the local newspaper said that his name had been "etched indelibly into the records of the North when he, with several companions, came upon that great hill of golden quartz that was immediately dubbed 'The Dome.' From that discovery was developed the famous Dome Mines of today, one of the greatest and most consistent producers of gold in the Timmins area." Again there was no indication as to whether it was an individual or a team that had made the initial discovery. Regardless of the discrepancies in the stories, Jack Wilson is generally credited with the discovery, as the team's failure or success was his responsibility.

Not only was the issue of the identity of Dome's actual discoverer clouded in doubt, but it was also difficult to attach a verifiable date to the beginning of that momentous twelve-month period. The records of those distant days are unclear in chronicling an exact day when the "Big Dome" was uncovered. There is one article, however, in the Dome Mines Company archives that does provide a date. Typed on a sheet of plain paper, signed by F.H. Hall, the Office Superintendent of Dome Mines, and dated June 8, 1939, is the following: "In conversation with Harry A. Preston, yesterday afternoon, he told me that while prospecting for John S. Wilson, on June 6, 1909, at four o'clock in the afternoon, he pulled up some moss on the 'Dome' and first discovered gold on that property."

E.D. Loney, financial editor of *The Northern Miner*, stated in a 1935 review of the Dome Mines operations:

> When Edwards read the news of the discovery in a newspaper in his club in Chicago, his enthusiasm knew no bounds. In frantic haste he boarded a train for Porcupine, and so great was his excitement that, before he reached his destination, he had sprained an ankle and nearly lost his life by drowning in a dash by canoe across Frederick House Lake. On meeting the prospectors and feasting his eyes on the gold, he dispatched his famous telegram to Dr. T.N. Jamieson of Chicago: 'Have discovered golden pole beyond description. Answer Matheson Wednesday, Haileybury Thursday. Protect cheques $6,000.'

The portly Edwards was not deterred by such minor mishaps as spraining his ankle or tumbling into the water when his canoe, with which he was not at all familiar, overturned; he simply had his prospector friends construct a makeshift stretcher of spruce limbs and boughs, on which he was borne to the Wilson camp. The first order of business following examination of the Big Dome was to arrive at a fair settlement with its discoverers. *The Northern Miner* reported the settlement which, in the absence of any other version, has been accepted by the authors of this book as essentially correct.

> The six prospectors, including Wilson, received $1,000 cash each for a three-eighth interest in the discovery claim, P. 1286, and a 50 per cent interest in the other claims. In addition, Wilson received an overriding 10 per cent interest in all the claims, as a bonus from the grubstaker.

The prospecting team then split up and each went his separate way. Wilson, of course, remained, becoming a member of the Board of Directors of the first Dome company. Preston, whose name was perpetuated by other mines in the

Porcupine area, eventually vanished from public view and "in later years went broke," according to Clary Dixon.

The stage was now set for the next major step: raising sufficient funds to finance a mine.

CHAPTER 3

The Fateful First Year

"Between the discovery and the payment of dividends lie the most interesting stages of mine-making," wrote E.D. Loney in *The Northern Miner*. The months following the sensational find in the Porcupine country were crucial indeed for the mine that soon became one of Canada's great gold producers.

W.S. Edwards was now faced with the problem of finding the large sums of money required to turn half a dozen mining claims deep in the wilderness of northern Ontario into a mine. Although he had made money in his plumbing business, Edwards, even in partnership with Dr. T.N. Jamieson, did not have enough to develop a mine. A week after completing arrangements with Wilson and the other prospectors, Edwards moved to Toronto where he set up his scheme for attracting financiers. In his rooms at the King Edward Hotel, he displayed the ore samples that he had brought with him from Porcupine, making it known that he would welcome calls from prospective investors. One visitor commented that Edwards' attitude toward his potential clients was that of a stern schoolmaster — he forbade cigar smoking in his rooms, and did not allow any interruptions during his presentation.

Weeks slipped by with no happy conclusion in sight. Edwards, journalists reported, had received many offers, but rejected them all. Presumably the offers were too low; men with money to invest, or even to speculate with, were cautious when it came to mining gold in Ontario. One potential investor was the firm of McCormick Bros. of New York City, represented in Canada by Walter Geddes, who, after hearing the lecture and seeing the ore specimens, suggested that Edwards negotiate directly with the McCormicks in New York. Edwards stubbornly insisted that if the McCormicks were interested, they should be willing to come to him. He demanded an advance of $5,000 for an option on the property, which Geddes reluctantly paid, but after inspecting the mining claims Geddes told his principals that he was disappointed with what he had seen and recommended that the option be dropped.

It was late in the winter of 1910 when Edwards met satisfactory investors.

According to Loney, in *The Northern Miner*: "It was nickel money, wrested from the ores of Sudbury, that financed the early development of Dome." In fact, Dome was financed by the private resources of the Monell Syndicate, whose principal members were the legendary Joseph de la Mar, one of the organizers of International Nickel of New Jersey, founded in 1902, and Ambrose Monell, who became its first president.

Just as it is uncertain who actually discovered the Big Dome, so there is uncertainty over how the New Jersey officials became involved in the high-risk financing of a gold mine. No doubt they had heard of the exciting events in the Porcupine area, close to their flourishing base metal operations at Sudbury. One story credits Joseph de la Mar with taking the initial step in the purchase of Dome. He was the typical "strong, silent man," and a decisive businessman who was always on the alert for profitable ventures. These qualities no doubt sparked his interest in the Dome property. While inspecting the Porcupine camp, de la Mar visited the Big Dome and, in his usual decisive manner, promptly declared, "We'll take it!", one of the lengthier statements made by a man of few words. He then hastened to New York to recommend the purchase to his associates.

Twenty years after the discovery of the Dome, Charles Denison, a prosperous Buffalo coal dealer with an eye for investing in mining in northern Ontario (in addition to his connection with Dome, Denison had established the Buffalo Mine at Cobalt and had taken an active part in the operation of Teck Hughes Gold Mines in Kirkland Lake), wrote notes which gave a somewhat different account of how "nickel money" launched Dome Mines.

Denison wrote that Sam Singlehurst, while doing exploration work for him in Ontario, drew his attention to the possibilities of the Edwards claims. Denison later met Edwards, whom he persuaded to go to New York where prospects for financing were more promising, and introduced him to Ambrose Monell. After three days of intense negotiations, during which the trio were joined by Jack Wilson, the first significant decision was made to telephone Toronto for the incorporation of a company to be called Dome Mines Company Limited. A twenty-page option contract was typed and the four men packed their bags for Toronto, where they were joined by Sam Singlehurst, Thomas Jones, superintendent of the Buffalo Mines, and an engineer named John Lawson, superintendent of the Canadian Copper Company at Copper Cliff. (De la Mar was not mentioned by Dension as having been part of this group at the time.) Because it was still winter, Edwards arranged for twenty-five men to clear away the snow at the Big Dome, the Golden Stairway and anything else that the group would want to examine. The prospective buyers studied the terrain with practised eyes — for a mine and for profit.

"Finally," wrote Charles Denison, "Mr. Monell and I sat on a log and thrashed out the whole proposition. We fully considered the fact that there had never been any paying gold mine in Ontario up to that date. We decided to purchase the property. On our way back, at Toronto, we made the first payment under the option."

The first payment was said to have been $35,000. Dome Mines Company Limited was incorporated by letters patent on March 23, 1910, and the Board of Directors consisted of W.S. Edwards, Dr. T.N. Jamieson, John S. Wilson, A.T. Struthers, and Alexander Fasken. Edwards was President, Wilson was Vice-President, and Fasken, a leading member of a distinguished Toronto law firm, was Secretary, a post he held until his death 34 years later.

Ambrose Monell was elected to the Board on January 4, 1911, and on March 22 was appointed Vice-President and General Manager. The Monell Syndicate agreed, at the time of incorporation, "to develop and operate the property at their expense," to a maximum cost of $375,000. Expenditures in excess of this amount would be paid by the Company.

The first Board of Directors continued in office until March 28, 1912, when Ambrose Monell became President. Edwards remained a Director, as did Jack Wilson, and signed the first Report to Shareholders, dated January 3, 1912, which covered the first year and a half of operations. The opening paragraphs read:

> The Dome Mines Company, Limited, is organized under the laws of the Province of Ontario. It owns 240 acres of patented lands in the township of Tisdale, Province of Ontario, known as Porcupine Mining District.
>
> The property was acquired by the issue of $2,500,000.00 of the Capital Stock of the Company at par, subject to a charge of $450,000.00 for which amount Bonds of the Company were issued . . .
>
> Subsequently, under date of August 29th, 1911, the Capital Stock of the Company was increased by the issue of $1,000,000.00 . . . the proceeds of this sale of stock . . . going into the treasury, out of which the above-mentioned bonds were retired.

The bonds had been issued for the "benefit of William S. Edwards, Thomas N. Jamieson, Frederick C. Remington, John S. Wilson, George Burns, Harry A. Preston, Frank N. Campbell, Gilbert Rheault, Ida M. Wilson and Ambrose Monell — in full satisfaction of all claims."

The Report to Shareholders listed as Directors E.C. Converse, J.R. de la Mar, C.L. Denison, W.S. Edwards, Alex Fasken, Ambrose Monell and J.S. Wilson.

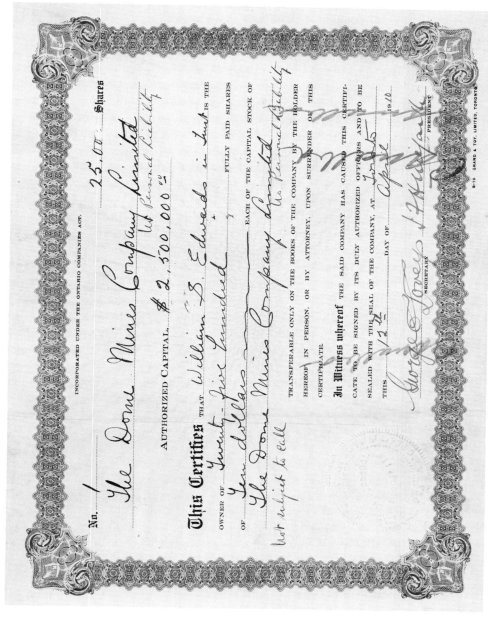

No. 1

25,000 Shares

The Dome Mines Company Limited
its personal liability

INCORPORATED UNDER THE ONTARIO COMPANIES ACT.

AUTHORIZED CAPITAL. $2,500,000

This Certifies THAT William S. Edwards in Trust IS THE

OWNER OF Twenty-five hundred

of Ten dollars FULLY PAID SHARES

EACH OF THE CAPITAL STOCK OF

The Dome Mines Company Limited its personal liability

not subject to call

TRANSFERABLE ONLY ON THE BOOKS OF THE COMPANY BY THE HOLDER
HEREOF IN PERSON, OR BY ATTORNEY, UPON SURRENDER OF THIS
CERTIFICATE.

In Witness whereof THE SAID COMPANY HAS CAUSED THIS CERTIFI-
CATE TO BE SIGNED BY ITS DULY AUTHORIZED OFFICERS AND TO BE
SEALED WITH THE SEAL OF THE COMPANY, AT Toronto

THIS 12th DAY OF April 19 10.

George Tovey   Philip K. Jaffray
SECRETARY   PRESIDENT

8-10 GRAND & TOY, LIMITED, TORONTO

Share certificate No. 1 of Dome Mines Company Limited, issued on April 12, 1910, to William S. Edwards.

William M. Mein, long experienced in the development of gold mines not only in America, but also in South Africa, was hired as Consulting Engineer to direct the work underground. Henry Hanson, previously with the Merrill Metallurgical Company of San Francisco, was also appointed to take charge of the mill operations.

The entry of the International Nickel men into a Porcupine gold venture was a great strengthening factor in the development of a gold mining industry in Ontario. Not only would they provide the money to develop the economy of the North, but they would also provide strong leadership and expertise, backed by their experience in operating successful mining operations less than two hundred miles away. These were important considerations, because many people, remembering past failures, were still skeptical, even though experienced businessmen like Monell, de la Mar and Denison were satisfied with the prospects.

One dubious editorial, published in the *Mining Journal* of London, England, in the spring of 1911, represents the prevailing attitude toward gold mining in Ontario:

> The greatest secrecy has prevailed regarding the results of development work that has been carried out in the Timmins (Hollinger) and Dome properties. The enormous quartz outcrop at the Dome property, with its spectacular showings of free gold, stimulated the imagination of many people, and the vague statements — and contradictory ones too — that have from time to time been published, have only served to enhance the mystery surrounding this supposed to be fabulously rich property. A few people, perhaps, are in possession of the actual facts regarding the value of the ore proved by the development work in the Dome. The high standing of the group of financiers who control this property lends colour to all the stories published, despite the fact that the owners have never made a public statement about the values disclosed by the development . . .
>
> As a matter of fact, the Porcupine deposits are by no means peculiar to that section of the world, but have been exploited with indifferent success elsewhere, and absolutely reliable information, based on results of sampling, indicate that most of the engineers who have visited the Porcupine have turned the camp down . . .
>
> The people interested in the Dome property have a record of success behind them in the mining world, which should go a

long way in reassuring one that the property has merit . . .

The history of gold mining in eastern Canada has been one of uniform financial failure; and if, for no other reason, caution should be exercised regarding the Porcupine field until developments have reached such a stage as to indicate with absolute certainty the possibilities of the district, not only superficially but in depth. Lenticular bodies of quartz showing gold do not necessarily make paying mines.

The news of Edwards' claims set off a rush of prospectors to the Porcupine district. So much vigorous activity took place in the camp that it was later put to Rev. Fr. Theriault, the popular parish priest, that he seemed to be the only inhabitant who hadn't done any prospecting. Smiling broadly, the Father denied that he was an exception. "Oh," he said breezily, "I did some prospecting work myself in the early days."

Within a few weeks, nearly all of Tisdale Township was staked, as well as much of the neighbouring townships of Whitney, Deloro, Ogden, Shaw, and Langmuir, with unscrupulous promoters in the prospectors' wake. Louis Huntoon, a mining engineer visiting the Porcupine camp, was disturbed by what he saw. The spectacular surface showings, he stated, "inflated the value of claims to such an extent that they changed hands at mine prices before the properties had been prospected and caused such remarks as: The price at which properties are sold is determined by the number of specks of gold and, in some cases, the price appears to be $50,000 per speck. Much of the stock of the Porcupine camp, as well as that of other mining districts, is worth no more than the paper upon which it is written."

Huntoon did add, however, that "the two principal properties which have been developed are the Dome and Hollinger mines. These properties may be classed as mines, and the capital stock of the companies will be returned with interest to the stockholders."

Months before Huntoon's remarks, the *Canadian Mining Journal*, a sober and responsible periodical, expressed its own concern:

> Those who have at heart the real good of mining in general and of Porcupine in particular strongly deprecate the stupid flotations that are now being advertised in the newspapers. When leading businessmen take an active part in selling to the public a risk that is based upon the opinion of an unauthenticated "engineer," it is high time to call a halt . . .
>
> The real work is being done by real engineers. Porcupine has struck her gait. Let her not be ridden by the frenzied financier.

A big problem facing would-be mine developers in late 1910 was the poor communication with the "outside." With no telegraph services or telephones, and mail delivery very poor or non-existent, as the *Canadian Mining Journal* stated, "It can be readily imagined that a delay of one or two weeks in transmitting a letter from Porcupine to Toronto, Montreal or New York might imply the difference between success and failure in putting through a mining deal."

Access into the Porcupine country was initially by canoe in summer and dog team in winter. The heavy machinery, equipment and supplies that followed had to be hauled by horse-drawn sled in the winter, as the frozen makeshift roads provided an excellent surface. In summer, however, these roads were often impassable, until the wagon tracks were developed into corduroy roads. K.P. Bernhard, one of Monell's subordinates from Sudbury and probably an accountant, wrote a fascinating first-person account of the difficulties of travel and life in the northern Ontario bush in the early 1900s:

> To get to the Dome I had to go to North Bay by train and spend the night there. Next morning I took an early train on the T. & N.O. Railway, travelled north to a place called Kelso, where we arrived about seven in the evening. At Kelso one had to stay overnight at a stopping place. They were too modest to call these places hotels. The walls between the rooms were of rough lumber and one could see through the cracks into adjoining rooms. The only conveniences in the room were a water pitcher, a basin, and a "john." At seven o'clock the next morning the jaunt to the Dome commenced.
>
> First there was a drive in a stage over 12 miles of corduroy road to Frederick House Lake (so named because a Hudson Bay Company trading post known as Frederick House once stood on the shore) . . . Naturally the horses did not go beyond a walk at any time. At Frederick House a small steamer or launch took us across the lake . . . Though my recollection of the trip is rather vague now, I think we had a launch trip along the Frederick House River . . . and we had at least two canoe trips, one across Bobs Lake and one across Indian Lake. The distance between each of the water trips was about three miles, and those distances had to be walked — a total of about 10 miles. The total distance from Kelso to the Dome camp was about 40 miles and the total travelling time about 12 hours, with arrival at the camp about seven o'clock in the evening . . .
>
> One did not attempt to make the trip from Kelso unaccompanied, I should make clear. One always had a guide, called a packer, for the country was all forest and the trails were not well

identifiable. The Dome had three packers. They would make the trip from camp to Kelso, say on a Monday; spend Tuesday at Kelso attending to various business matters, and make the trip back on Wednesday. The packers carried the drill cores and the mail.

The canoe route described by Bernhard was "for the most part easy travelling," according to James Bartlett, an Ontario government geologist. It may have been child's play for a strapping young man, but it certainly was not easy for a mine builder, who needed something more efficient than canoes, sleighs and dog teams.

As the inadequacy of present methods became apparent, increased pressure was placed on the Ontario government to improve the means of transportation. Fortunately, T. & N.O. chairman Jacob Englehart was quick to act. Early in 1910 he instructed that a survey be made of the possible opportunities for business development and the resulting traffic potential to and from the Porcupine camp.

Arthur Cole, the T. & N.O. mining engineer, recommended that a branch line be built into the camp where, he said, the "leading properties were held by companies headed, for the most part, by experienced mining men from whom could be expected a progressive and, at the same time, rational development." As a result, the government of Premier John Whitney directed that the T. & N.O. run a 30-mile line from its main north-south track at a point between Matheson and Nellie Lake. Iroquois Falls, situated about two and one-half miles north of Kelso, was chosen as the junction point. After learning that the Abitibi Power and Paper Company had already named its company town Iroquois Falls, a new name was invented, Porquis, a combination of Porcupine and Iroquois.

In December, 1910, work began, with completion set for July 1, 1911, at an estimated cost of $450,000. Adding to the hardships, five feet of snow fell in the early months of 1911, which had to be shovelled by hand to clear the way for construction. The shortage of manpower was so great that prisoners serving light sentences as far away as North Bay were brought in to assist in the snow removal. By mid-June the tracks reached Golden City at the north end of Porcupine Lake where the builders encountered a sink-hole. Hundreds of tons of gravel had to be dumped in order to make the ground firm enough for the rails and before the hole was filled, two railway gravel cars jumped the tracks and disappeared into the muskeg.

By the end of June, 1911, the T. & N.O. had achieved its goal — the railway was ready to serve the Dome as well as neighbouring mines, and the "Muskeg Special," a flatcar rebuilt to carry the guests into the heart of the newly opened

No. 1 and No. 2 shafts
in 1910. (right)

The Dome property in 1910.
(centre)

Hitting the trail into
Porcupine before the
railway. (below)

HITTING THE TRAIL AT
TIMMINS. ONT

mining country, was dispatched from Porquis to help celebrate the occasion.

When Ambrose Monell and his New York associates departed from Porcupine following their decision to purchase the property, they left behind John Lawson, superintendent of the Canadian Copper Company plant at Copper Cliff (incorporated into International Nickel Company of Canada a few years later). Lawson's job was to develop the property for production. Even before the railway reached South Porcupine, Dome and its neighbours, Hollinger and McIntyre, the "big three" of the Porcupine camp, were nearing the production stage.

The Ontario Bureau of Mines, in its 1910 report, said little of Dome except that "no work was done on these claims other than some stripping . . . and active development work began under the supervision of Mr. John Lawson of the Canadian Copper Company." The report also noted that "a plant was taken in before the break-up and is now in operation." Nevertheless, by the end of 1910, Dome had "produced" 214 ounces of gold and 19 ounces of silver valued at $4,300 from the hand cobbing of 247 tons of high-grade ore. Although not an outstanding amount when compared with the sizable costs that Dome had incurred, it was an encouraging sign.

In contrast, the Bureau of Mines' report for 1911 described Dome in prosaic and exact terms. The six claims were located "in the first concession of Tisdale Township and included parts of lots 4 and 5, with the main workings on the northwest 40 acres of lot 4."

> In an area which is roughly 600 feet wide, north and south, and 800 feet long, east and west, there are frequent occurrences of quartz in irregular masses and narrow quartz veins, in some of which there is visible gold. Toward the east end of the workings there are large dome-like masses of quartz, in contact with Huronian conglomerates and slate-like greywacke, while to the west the quartz occurs chiefly as narrow veinlets associated with Keewatin schist which is impregnated with carbonate. The country rock in the proximity of the veins contains considerable crystallized iron pyrites.

Serious exploration work now began, with seven diamond drills brought in to probe various points on the property to an average depth of 450 feet.

Diamond drilling is a rapid and valuable method of securing rock samples from hundreds of feet below the surface. This method of exploration involves cutting a cylindrical section of rock (usually one to two inches in diameter) by using a drill bit set with diamonds which, while rotating at a high speed, is forced downward, pushing the core up the core barrel at the same time. The rate of progress slows as depth is attained because of the necessity of removing the

*Mill under construction in
spring of 1911. (top)*

*Foundation for the mill in
the spring of 1911. (centre)*

*Dome plant buildings in
the spring of 1911. (below)*

drill rods at 20-foot intervals to obtain core. Water is vital to the operation, as it is needed to wash away the cuttings and to keep the bit cool, and must therefore be pumped to a tank near the drill. A small pumping unit with a capacity of about 600 gallons per hour is used for this purpose.

The trenching and diamond drilling yielded spectacular results. Although Company records of the trenching give only limited assay results, there was considerable coarse gold in evidence and the more complete drill logs describe sections of ore grade material in detail. While these appear to have included several sections of low grade ore, the pattern of the orebodies within the geological structure was not worked out for several years. The early phase of development proceeded on the assumption that large zones would have to be mined. Initially, several small vertical shafts were sunk together with a double-tracked decline on a grade which varied from -13 to -18 degrees for a total length of 568 feet. Levels were established at depths of 45 and 100 feet, where the ore was divided into 100-foot rectangular blocks by drifts and cross-cuts. A number of raises were then driven to the surface and a chute was installed at the bottom of each. The ore, which was broken down from above in benches, was drawn off through these chutes, trammed by mules to the decline and hoisted to the surface. Inverted cone-shaped excavations were gradually formed, coming together to make one large open pit, or "glory hole," as the miners called it. No timber was necessary except for building chutes and shaft compartments.

There was much activity at other mine sites in the Porcupine area during this time. More and more seekers of gold swarmed through the bush and traversed the lakes, rivers and creeks west of the railway line. A.G. Burrows, assistant provincial geologist, summarized his view of the Porcupine country during this period:

> Lying along the southern fringe of the great clay belt of northern Ontario, it adjoins a prospective farming country. In this belt many townships have been laid out in six- and nine-mile squares and subdivided into mile blocks; in the gold area itself and in the adjoining country to the north many quarter sections (160 acres) have been granted to veterans (of the South African War) as homesteads. Up to the present time (1911) prospecting and development have shown that Tisdale is by far the most important township, while promising discoveries have been made in other townships in the vicinity, including Whitney, Ogden, Shaw, Deloro, and Langmuir . . .
>
> To the south and southeast of Tisdale a number of townships have been outlined into six-mile blocks during the past year, and these boundary lines furnish good ties for prospectors who are examining the outlying areas.

*Locomotives for surface
haulage of ore to crushing
plant. (above)*

Collar of 20 degree decline. (below)

In 1910 seven townsites were laid out near Porcupine Lake, with three becoming settlements of size and importance, of which two continue to flourish. At the northeast corner of the lake a community called Porcupine City began to grow, which today stands as the town of Porcupine. The *Souvenir Booklet Celebrating the Golden Anniversary of the Porcupine Gold Rush* describes the reaction of two weary prospectors approaching the freshly painted sign which proclaimed "Porcupine City":

> "Porcupine!" scoffed the one, "that's too bristly and slow a name for a new town." The other newcomer fairly sneered at the word "City." "Why, they haven't even got around to outside plumbing yet!" he said.

Baseball soon became the favourite sport of the booming town, and within a few years hockey, skiing, skating, snowshoeing, sleighing, hunting, fishing, boating, tennis, football, golf and curling occupied the leisure time of the Porcupine inhabitants.

In later years, "Lap" Laprairie's Turkey and Oyster Stags were rivalled only by the "Molly Hogan" festivities at Golden City, which provided free music and "eatables and drinkables" for all, or perhaps by some of the Canadian Legion events. If one were interested in perfecting one's dancing technique, Mrs. Bagshaw would gladly give lessons, and dancing recitals would be presented to admiring audiences.

Although mining was the community's major industry, several entrepreneurs soon established themselves to serve the population. J. Conlan purveyed cold spring water at five cents a pail, summer and winter, and kept track of his "accounts" by notching the doorposts of those who owed. Bert Dewar operated the first greenhouse and could never understand why people wouldn't eat spinach. "I can't even give it away," he would complain. Jamieson Meat, Olton's bakery and Wernick's cigar and sundries would provide most of the basic necessities, and if one ailed, Charlie See's "Pills and Things" would be sure to have a cure. A nearby amusement parlor, operated by T. Ryan and "Brick" Duke in a large tent, was often quickly converted into an opera house by simply hanging out a sign which boasted "Lyric Theatre."

Nearby was the settlement of Pottsville, which grew around the Shuniah Hotel, which served the Scottish-Ontario mine and was operated by Major Potts and his wife. Major Potts wanted the new town to bear the name of Shuniah, the Indian word for gold, but Mrs. Potts preferred Pottsville. A "compromise" was finally reached, and Pottsville it remained until the community became absorbed by the rapidly expanding town of Porcupine.

There were no plans for a town to serve the Dome mine until it was announced that the T. & N.O.'s branch line would be built near the lake's south

The "glory hole" (open pit) from which much of Dome's gold was mined in the early years.

shore and close to Dome. Two enterprising and far-sighted entrepreneurs, A.C. Brown and his partner, Clifford Moore, laid out a townsite at that location which later became South Porcupine, and soon became the leading community in the Porcupine Lake region, developing into a base for Dome. As business tended to move south, the settlements of Golden City, Porcupine and Pottsville soon found themselves on the wrong side of the lake for commercial purposes.

Many travellers wonder how the name of Porcupine originated. One story says that an early mapmaker noted the approximate shape of a porcupine in the lake's outline. Another says that 19th century travellers paddling across the lake were struck by the likeness of thorn-like clumps of weed on the rocky shoreline to a porcupine's quills. Regardless of its origin, everyone used "Porcupine" to refer to both the lake and the whole mining district.

The first signs of urban life appeared as streets were laid out and rough but serviceable houses, restaurants, stores and banks were erected. Dome's management looked forward to a prosperous year ahead, as did the operators of other mines in the region. There was not a cloud to be seen — yet.

*Clouds of smoke over
Porcupine Lake on July 11,
1911. (above)*

*The fire advances on South
Porcupine. (below)*

CHAPTER 4

Hurricane of Fire

A warm, dry spring arrived early in 1911. The wet, spongy muskeg became as dry as tinder and needed only a tiny spark to set it and the dense coniferous bush surrounding the mine and the townsites alight. This happened on numerous occasions, as isolated fires began to break out in the southwestern areas of the sprawling Porcupine camp in early May. The Hollinger mine, half a dozen miles west of the Dome, was the first major victim, despite the best efforts of the Hollinger crews. The entire operation was destroyed just as it was about to move into production.

Throughout June and the beginning of July small fires burned in Bristol, Deloro, Whitney and Tisdale townships, developing into a real threat to Dome. By the second week of July, the fires had merged into an immense conflagration 12 to 14 miles wide, moving menacingly to the northeast, where the Dome, South Porcupine and neighbouring settlements lay. Firefighting crews were organized to beat out the flames creeping up on the Dome boundaries. One serious fire which threatened the entire Dome complex was extinguished by the combined vigour of no fewer than 200 men from the mine crews.

By this time a great deal of development had been completed on the Dome property: the 12-drill compressor provided all the air needed for underground mining, and the construction of the 40-stamp mill was moving ahead on schedule; two shafts, 250 feet apart, were already sunk a quarter of the way down to their planned depth of 500 feet.

Then dawned the dreadful morning of July 11. A mild southwest wind became "a hurricane, travelling at a velocity of about 70 miles per hour, quickly fanning to roaring torrents of flame the many smouldering fires in the district," according to Toronto mining engineer G.R. Rogers. The *Canadian Mining Journal* called it "a cyclone fanning all the combustible materials in the virgin forest till it was like a blast furnace." The people of South Porcupine, watching in paralyzed terror the tremendous billows of smoke blackening the southwestern sky, heard the prolonged whistle blast of the Dome plant shortly after one o'clock. It was an urgent warning to flee, as the danger to the area was very great.

Flames 150 feet high swept over the property like a fiery tidal wave. Ten employees lost their lives and all surface buildings and equipment were destroyed. The conflagration raged unchecked with horrendous winds and blinding, suffocating smoke. The *Canadian Mining Journal* reported: "At the Dome Mines, where 160 acres were swept clear of trees, the air was on fire. Flames shot out of the various buildings at once and men fighting the blaze were quickly surrounded and ringed in. Three-quarters of the loss of life was due directly to the attempt to beat back the waves of heat and smoke."

The fire leaped from the mine to the town and the men, women and children of South Porcupine began running for their lives, racing down the main street to plunge into Porcupine Lake. Many of them drowned when the churning waves, whipped by the heat-laden wind, tore the weaker ones from the logs and other debris to which they clung. There were many heroic exploits that day, some of which are described on the first page of the Cobalt *Daily Nugget*, reproduced in this volume.

Surviving women and children were quickly picked up and moved in canoes, rowboats and motor launches to the relative safety of the lake's north side. The fire swept across the lake, engulfing almost all of Pottsville, but, by some strange chance, destroying only a few houses on the fringe of Golden City. The refugees cowering there went through still another frightening experience when a railway car, holding blasting powder and 350 cases of dynamite, exploded and blew a hole 15 feet deep and 47 feet wide in the rocky soil.

One vivid eyewitness account is given by J.P. Bartleman, who later became active in municipal government in Timmins:

> For several days fires could be seen in the distance but at the time there didn't seem to be much danger. Then, on the morning of July 11, a strong wind blew up and by 11 o'clock you could see the smoke rising from the fires in the bush, tremendous circles of smoke rising high into the sky. Darkness fell over us, and, as the flames drew nearer, everyone began to fight the fire in every way possible, to save our new town. But the houses began to go up in flames by two in the afternoon. Many of us, instead of joining the fire fighters, made sure all the women and children were away from the buildings and sent as many of them as possible in boats out into the lake.
>
> First thing that morning I dug a trench by my house, in which I could bury my valuables if we should be in real danger. When it was clear that we were all in peril, I hurried home to use the

Bucket brigade at work in South Porcupine, July 9, 1911.

Northern Ontario
The Land of
Opportunity

The Cobalt Daily Nugget

The Richest Mining
District on the
Continent

VOL. III. No. 143   4 O'Clock Edition   COBALT, ONTARIO, FRIDAY JULY 14, 1911   PROBS:—PROBS:—Fair and decidedly cool to-day and to-morrow   Price 5 cents

LIST OF DEAD IN PORCUPINE FIRE WILL NOT EXCEED 200 PERSONS

Known Dead, Most of Whose Bodies Have Been Recovered, Now Reaches Fifty-four---Nearly All Victims Were Buried in Porcupine---Bodies Brought in From Redstone and Many Others Reported Lying in Bush Throughout Fire-swept Area

WHERE ARE PROSPECTORS IN BRISTOL AND DENTON?

No Definite Word From Cripple Creek Where Fires Were Very Bad---Relatives in Outside Point's Frantically Calling For Information---The Relief Situation To-day

KNOWN DEAD

JULES METAYER, French Consul, Montreal, aged 30. Not recovered
ANDRE LA HUE, was waiter in Metropole Hotel, Montreal, formerly of Paris France, aged 31, not recovered.
ARPILA MONDOUX, Cobalt, aged 31, recovered from Porcupine Lake.
CHARLES E. ADAMS, Phoenixville, Pa., aged 21, recovered
   TAYLOR, shoemaker, Pearl Lake, not recovered
MACE SMITH, New Liskeard, not recovered.
R. A. DWYER, of Idaho, walled at Dome, Porcupine Gold Mines. Buried there.
FREDERICK LAKE, old time prospector, formerly of Bracebridge, buried there.
ANDY TOULL, superintendent of United Porcupine Gold Mines, formerly of Bracebridge, buried on property with Masonic honors.
JOE FLETCHER, Cockermouth, Cumberland County, England, aged 31, recovered, and buried on United Porcupine property.
PATRICK DWYER, opening a boardinghouse.
WILLIAM MOORE, Cobalt, aged 38, not recovered
MERVIN STRAIN, relatives in Porcupine.
NATHAN HAAS, aged 38, of Spokane, Washington, not recovered
STANLEY NICHOLSON, of Guelph, aged 28, not recovered
WILLIAM GOHR, aged 43, formerly of Pembroke, recovered.
TOM B. GRIDER, 34, recovered, Haileybury.
HARRY HANDY, Dome Mine, native of Bath, England.
FRITZ MANCH, nothing known.
JOHN WHATMAUGH, aged 22, student at Toronto University.
   Buried there
THOMAS J. KING, aged 45, of Coppercliff, buried
THOMAS JACKSON, American, colored, buried
ARCHER JOHNSTON, Sudbury, buried.
JOSEPH AHA, 39, Finlander from Dome Mine, died on train.
DEPALI DEPPIG, Syrian, died in Liskeard Hospital.
LMO M. BULMAN, London, England, sampler at Dome, body shipped.
HARRY FITZMAUGE, aged 27, of Melbourne, not recovered
ROBERT WEISS, West Dome, aged 40, of Butte Montana, recovered.
MIKE WATSON, same place.
MIKE BRADIO, WEISS aged three years.
JAMES RENNIE, 81 Farley Avenue, Toronto.
JAMES WELCH, aged 32, of Cache Bay.
JOHN McLAUGHLIN, body shipped to Cobalt.
WILLIAM KING, Elk City, Idaho.
ANGUS McDONALD, Turner Street, Ottawa.
A. B. BURT, sampler at West Dome.
MRS. A. E. BURT.
JACK TAYLOR, first year mining student at Toronto.
N. McQUEEN, carpenter, West Dome.
MRS. D. M. McQUEEN
JOHN WALL
MANBY BROOKINS.
JOHN SAUNDE.
JOHN DRETSON.
HUGH McLEOD, of Glencoe Mills, Cape Breton.
IBROWN HENNINGER.
J. V. CRANSHAW.
WILLIAM McLEAN.
J. PAULIN.
J. GEE.
F. SMETA.
(The preceding 24 people being from the West Dome)
B. PY RYAN, of Lowell, Mass.
CAPT. THOMAS DUNBAR, of Kennedy & Dunbar, South Porcupine
R. THERIAN.

[rest of column illegible]

Plunged Into Lake To Escape Flames

Fire Missing at King Porcupine Mines Including the Cook

Stories of those who perished in Porcupine, whose causes are unknown and many never be known, still come in. Daniel Vert, a New York mining engineer, but one of the most harrowing experiences of those who escaped the fire without injury. Yoel and Burdick were in Shack when the fire swept into that district. They had just time to reach Goose Lake on the King-Porcupine Mines property, the first claim ever staked on the Porcupine district, and plunging into the lake remained submerged until the flames had swept around them and the dense clouds of smoke cleared away.

[remainder illegible]

Race For Life of Vipond's 30 Employes

Capt. Jack Leckie and Bert Rea Tell a Vivid Story of Escape

Capt. Jack Leckie and Bert Rea returned to town yesterday from Porcupine, where they went through the fire without the slightest injury. The many friends of these two young men were rather anxious about their safety, as no word had been received in the camp as to their whereabouts.

[remainder illegible]

Injured by Dynamite And Hand Cut by Axe

On a Nipissing Central car, on his way to Haileybury, was a more boy. He was about twelve or thirteen years of age with his left hand in a bandage and another one around his head.

[remainder illegible]

FOUR MISSING PARTNERS.

[illegible]

List of Patients, Liskeard Hospital

The following is a list of those admitted into Lady Minto Hospital at New Liskeard, up to last night:
Jean Karette, Cochrane.
Mrs. Nickolas Perry, Cochrane.
Sylvester Irisuher, Cochrane.
Mrs. Desjardine, Cochrane.
Baby Desjardine (36 hrs old), Cochrane.
W. Mason, Cochrane.
A. Bush, Milberta.
Mrs. Ferris, Cochrane.
Baby Ferris (3½ hrs old), Cochrane.
John B[.]ue, Porcupine.
Victor Mackie, Dome, Porcupine.
D. G. Bisset, Strathcona.
Edgar A. Shakespeare, 605 Yonge street, Toronto.
J. S. Taylor, White Horse, Y.T.
W. Johns, Dome, Porcupine.
Alex. Faulkner, Copper Cliff, Ont.
Tom Cooper, 11 Petar street, Toronto
J. J. Vanasse, Chichester, Que.
John B[.]ue, Porcupine.
M. Therian, Ottawa.
   Johnson, Porcupine.
The husband and two other children of Mrs. Desjardine are still at Porcupine.

Bodies Of Five Men Recovered From Fire

Remains of Capt. Dunbar, Tom Geddes And Wm. Gohr Identified

The bodies of the five men burned to death in the store at South Porcupine have all been recovered and

MANY ANXIOUS INQUIRIES.

57 MEN SAVED LIVES BY STANDING IN RESERVOIR

Henry Hanson, Supt. of Construction at Dome, Tells of Narrow Escapes and Harrowing Scenes at West Dome Where Loss Was Great

Mr. Henry Hanson, superintendent of construction at the Dome property, tells a graphic story of the fire and its destruction on the Dome and West Dome properties. Mr. Hanson had a narrow escape from death, along with several others, and he relates facts as they actually occurred.

[remainder illegible]

Thirteen Proved To Be Lucky Number

Experience of Party on East Shore of Night Hawk Lake Tuesday

Haileybury, July 14.—On a rocky point on the east shore of Night Hawk Lake, in the township of Thomas, about thirteen men on Tuesday afternoon, wondering if the flames would reach them. The route ran has the legend of lucky number, not on Tuesday it proved a lucky thirteen to the party who unhesitatingly by the flames. They were composed of Haileybury prospectors to whom cost. Thomas township home of the party was Ed. Grote, Dan Froood, Harry Hounslution and Dave Allen. They came round to the Thomas their lives from the fire in the Thomas township, and could see the smoke from Porcupine curling upwards on the other side of Night Hawk Lake.

[remainder illegible]

Will Reorganize the Cobalt Central Mines

Philadelphia Syndicate, the Present Owners, Will Hold Special Meeting Shortly To Discuss Affairs

The syndicate of Philadelphia stock-holders of the Cobalt Central Mines Company, which last week bought in for $100,000 the Standard Cobalt properties at Cobalt, will meet early next week to map out plans for the future. The syndicate has deposited 10 per cent. of the purchase price with the Canadian liquidator, E. H. C. Clarkson, and will devise a plan by which Cobalt Central stockholders will have an equal opportunity to participate in the new organization by contributing to the fund necessary to complete the payment for the property and restore the mine to the operating class. The Cobalt Central is the holding company for the Standard Cobalt Mines, Limited.

[remainder illegible]

Shores of the Lake Strewn With Trunks

It is surprising the number of park-works, and cases, trunks, etc., that have been found in Porcupine Lake, said one survivor, in speaking to The Daily Nugget. Around South Porcupine there are hundreds of them lying in the water.

[remainder illegible]

ditch and found that someone else had already filled it. Except for what I could jam into a suitcase, I had to leave everything behind. At the lake, I left the bag as close to the water as I could, but the wind drove the water back from shore, and the suitcase was burned, as were hundreds of others that had been left on the shore. But even those who had buried their valuables could not be sure their things were safe. If they dug their trench in haste and did not cover it over properly, and if any cloth was near the surface, the fire would simply burn its way down and consume everything in the trench.

For two hours, while the fire was at its height, Bartleman clung to a tree by the water's edge until the flames died away. That night he slept on the floor of a bakery which had miraculously escaped destruction. "It was hot that day and very cold that night. Many people became ill with pneumonia," he recalled. "Undoubtedly many suffered permanent ill effects and perhaps found their lives considerably shortened by the experience and the hardships they endured."

When this terrible day was finally over, seven South Porcupine men were missing, presumably drowned in the lake. At the West Dome Mine, an unrelated neighbour of Dome Mines, the Manager, Robert Weiss, his wife and child, and almost all of the mine's employees – numbering between fifteen and twenty – died by asphyxiation after taking refuge at the bottom of the mine shaft, 80 feet below the surface; the oxygen had been sucked from the shaft to feed the voracious fire above them.

The death toll of the fire is usually given as 73, but veteran prospectors have long insisted that this number must be much greater, perhaps even reaching 200. This doubt is understandable because, at that time, it was almost impossible to arrive at an exact figure for the area's population. Fortune-seekers were pouring in daily, and others were departing for the bush as soon as they had picked up supplies and equipment. Many prospected alone in the woods and could have died in the fire without anyone knowing their fate. Property damage was reported as amounting to $3 million, which might also have been underestimated, as Dome Mines alone suffered a loss of nearly half a million dollars.

Another recollection is provided by Charles Richardson, who had already been prospecting for twenty years and who had occasionally worked at the young Dome mine at the time of the fire. When the conflagration began to threaten the settlements at Porcupine Lake, Richardson was prospecting with a crew in Whitney Township. The veteran of two or three forest fires and well aware of the dryness of the bush that summer, Richardson sensed the peril when he felt the wind rising. "We decided then and there to bury our prospect-

Wreckage of the Dome power plant. (above)

Shaft house and crusher photographed immediately after the fire. (below)

ing gear and make for the lake," he said. "The outskirts of Golden City were on fire when we got there. I went on to Pottsville to get my trunk and suitcase at the Potts house, where I had left them. By this time, I had dragged that luggage out of the way of fires so often it got so it would follow me!"

Help for the stricken area was prompt and generous. The T. & N.O., which had itself lost four construction camps, along with rolling stock and other equipment, moved the injured to hospitals as far away as Toronto, at no charge. The T. Eaton Co. in Toronto shipped a railway car loaded with tents, blankets, clothing and other necessities, which arrived in South Porcupine the day after the fire.

A great surge of sympathy, expressed in tangible ways, came from other companies and private individuals in southern Ontario. For days, T. & N.O. trains trundled northwards with supplies for the homeless. Henry Hanson, the Mill Superintendent at Dome at the time, recalled his experiences in an article written for the *Canadian Mining Journal* thirty-six years later:

> To me, going through the Porcupine fire towers above all other experiences. Four of us took shelter on the rock dump excavated from the mill site. The wind was blowing from the west, and, as Edwards Lake was directly west of our position, we were out of the path of the smoke, heat, and the gases distilled from the burning timber. During a tense two hours we fully realized that if the wind shifted a bit to the south we would get not only the smoke and the heat from the forest fire but also that from the burning mill, and our position would become untenable. As one of our party remarked, our lives wouldn't have been worth a plugged nickel.

Golden City, which had survived the fire virtually intact, was jammed with refugees. Some boarded T. & N.O. trains destined for Sudbury and Copper Cliff, where they received medical attention, if required, and stayed until fully recovered from their terrifying experience. Hanson recalled:

> On the second day after the fire, a private car arrived at Golden City, bringing Ambrose Monell, Frank Ludlam, and others from New York; A.P. Turner, Captain Lawson (who had directed the first work at Dome after the New Yorkers took control), and George Sylvester of Copper Cliff. The next morning (the third day after the fire), as many as could pile on to a section handcar made their way to within a mile of the mine and made it on foot the rest of the way. Others went by boat to what had been South Porcupine and then walked to the Dome, a distance of some two miles.

A HERO OF THE PORCUPINE FIRE

BY BEN HUGHES

A LONDON despatch reads: "The King has approved of the Albert medal of the second-class being conferred upon Edward Bell of the Canadian Copper Company for gallantry in connection with the disastrous fire in South Porcupine."

Just as many of the records of the possessors of the Victoria Cross occupy in the official records but a few lines of space, so does this bald announcement of a richly-deserved honor fail to convey the reader any conception of the scene where Edward Bell proved his manhood. It is strange that, when so many apocryphal dramas of narrow escape were recorded during the horrible fire at Porcupine last July, nothing was said of the escape of the little knot of people round Mr. H. C. Meek's house at the Dome.

It is a matter of record now how from one end of northern Ontario to the other the people had to flee for their lives and equally a matter of knowledge how brave men refused to own that they were beaten, and so endangered in many cases lost their lives. At the Dome the week before the fateful July 11 they had had a tough fight with fire and had dug a reservoir in the centre of the property to supply water for the pipes that had been laid from one end of the property to the other. When therefore the fire leaped down on the Dome from the bush that hot afternoon Mr. Meek and everyone else thought they were well prepared to meet it, and he and his staff fought it till the last gasp. He remained so long, in fact, that he did not arrive back at his own house, where his wife, his wife's mother, Mrs. Paddock, and his two children were, before the flames had leaped clear over the intervening space which had been cleared and set his house on fire. With him were F. Battersby, D. G. Bissett, L. H. Solman and a man named Cooper, all of the Dome staff.

Mr. Meek rushed into the house, told his family of their peril and threw open the front door to lead them out. The whole of the house front was on fire. He dashed to the back and found that the woodshed had caught, too, and escape was cut off there. He determined to break through the flames from the front, but the gust which met him as he threw open the door decided him that, if he could win his way through, the women and children certainly could not, and he turned back in despair. For the first time fortune aided him now. Opening the back door, he found that the furious wind had shifted and that it now blew the flames away from the door so that the whole party could get out. Anything was better than to be cremated in that flaming house, and out they all went together, the men dragging the women, with their clothes already on fire, and the women protecting the children, both only just able to walk. Just a few yards from the back door stood six rain barrels half full. On that stony knoll of the Dome Mr. Meek found a little soil and every day he had watered some grass seed he had sown. It was therefore green and did not so easily catch fire as the surface mould and vegetation. At this time the whole party, only dreamed of getting out so that they could die in the fresh air; they were hemmed in by flames, their vitality was sapped by inhaling the gaseous fumes which preceded and accompanied the fire and hope had gone. Only it was better, they felt, to die on the rock near water, if they could not reach it, than in that crackling furnace of a house. So they lay down huddled in each others' arms near the water barrels while the smoke hung so thick that they could not see many yards and the air was full of fire.

Solman, who had come to aid the Meek party, tried to reach the reservoir where so many men saved their lives, but the flames caught him, and that afternoon he was found dead not fifty feet from the water barrels. Cooper ran to the west and reached the lake, but he died in New Liskeard hospital in a few days; the others, fortunately, had no longer power to move. Mr. Meek says that he can just remember seeing a face appear out of the smoke and a minute afterwards he felt a splash of

EDWARD BELL.

water on his face. It was Edward Bell, who was ladling water out of the barrels with his old, soft felt hat. Then he lost consciousness. He learned from Bell afterwards, though the foreman carpenter of the Dome does not talk much about the incident, that when he arrived Mrs. Meek's skirt and foot were on fire, and that he first applied himself to putting it out. Then, coolly and calmly, while the fire swept all living organisms out of existence all around him and the hot air scorched the lungs, he continued to dip into the barrels, souse himself and distribute the water impartially over the prostrate figures round him.

The fire was at its height at 2 o'clock, at 4 the danger was over, and Edward Bell and a few square inches of grass had saved seven people. They had grazed death, but they were alive mainly because Edward Bell walked out of a zone of comparative safety into a whirlwind of smoke and flame and for a full hour, never knowing when he would be roasted alive, with a level head and a steady hand, threw water out of his old hat wherever he saw a spark fall or a flame burst out on the exhausted figures round the water barrels.

Edward Bell still works at the Dome, and it is safe to say that the men who work for him and those who work with him know nothing of this story, for he is not that kind of man: he acts, he doesn't talk. But Mr. Meek did talk, and he talked to

Mr. A. R. Turner, the general manager of the Canadian Copper Company at Copper Cliff. Mr. Turner took the matter up whole-heartedly and laid the facts before the Carnegie Hero Fund and the British authorities. A few days ago the news despatches told of the honor Edward Bell had received at the hands of the King, and it is hard to see how it would be possible for a man to more deserve the reward and medal from Mr. Andrew Carnegie than Edward Bell.

SPOT ON DOME MINE WHERE EDWARD BELL SAVED SEVEN PEOPLE.
From a photo taken immediately after the fire.

DOME WATER TANK, IN WHICH 57 LIVES WERE SAVED IN PORCUPINE FIRE.

The above article, reproduced from the original issue of The Globe, *of Toronto, in 1912, describes the royal honour bestowed upon Edward Bell for his gallantry during the Porcupine fire of 1911.*

The party and the private car stayed on for two days. Much of the time was spent at the Dome, viewing the ruins and making decisions as to what of the mill and mine and powerhouse equipment could be salvaged. Stamps, tube mills and filter presses on concrete foundations came through without serious damage.

Hanson was impressed with life on the private car, where he stayed for several days. The car, he explained, was of "special design" — one half consisting of berths and staterooms, the other half of dining room and kitchen — "specially suited for frontier life." Hanson was invited to return to Toronto with the New York group; this, he said, "made it possible for me to get to know the powers-that-be better than under normal conditions." In Toronto, Hanson stopped at the Queen's Hotel (on the site of the present Royal York). After buying a new wardrobe to replace that lost in the fire, and taking a three-day trip on Lake Ontario "for relaxing," Hanson was back on the job at the Dome in just one week.

The Dome property began humming with reconstruction activity. Immediate action was taken to get the compressor back into service, which was accomplished in about a month, thanks to help given by men loaned by the Canadian Copper Company. Six weeks after the fire 500 men were working. When the Board of Directors met in January, 1912, they were presented with a report by Edwards which outlined the extensive work that had already been carried out:

> In July, 1911, the plant was destroyed by fire and $309,236.35, the approximate amount of the loss after deducting salvage, was collected as insurance.
>
> The plant under construction at the present time consists of 40 stamps with the necessary tube mills and cyanide equipment, estimated to handle between 350 and 400 tons daily.
>
> The powerhouse is designed with sufficient excess power to operate a mill with double the capacity of the one at present installed.
>
> The mill, rock house, and powerhouse are all of steel and concrete construction and absolutely fireproof. The storehouse, laboratory, etc., are also of steel and brick and fireproof.
>
> The houses of the various superintendents, foremen, and miners are of brick with galvanized iron roofs as well as the hospital, club house, eating camps, etc.
>
> The construction of its own railroad spur . . . from the Temiskaming and Northern Ontario Railroad to the mill site has

been completed.

From the present indications the mill will be in operation some time in the latter part of February, 1912.

. . . From the beginning of operations, the cost of the plant, equipment, and development, after deducting . . . insurance, was $860,352.26. Of this amount, $375,000.00 was expended by the Monell Syndicate prior to April 22, 1911, and was not charged against the Company.

Edwards proved accurate in his forecast as the mill was completed on schedule. Milling began in March and the Company celebrated the event with a sumptuous banquet with the new President, Ambrose Monell, in the chair. These festivities were described in later years by the Timmins *Daily Press* as "one of the grandest occasions in the early history of the Porcupine," and were organized by the executives of the Dome mine and the South Porcupine Board of Trade "to show the Directors of Dome, prominent mining men from all over Canada, Members of Parliament, and representatives of a number of Canadian newspapers, that the Golden Porcupine was just that." The *Daily Press* continued:

Twenty-one private railway cars were hired to carry guests from as far away as New York City and Chicago, and an additional 20 cars were provided by the Pullman Company.

The Board of Trade hired a Toronto company to look after street decorations, and patriotic citizens added individual touches to their own homes and businesses. Imagine the effect of these elaborate decorations on the rough buildings and tents newly erected after the disastrous fire, less than a year before!

On the evening before the guests were treated to a Grand Smoking Concert at the Rex Theatre in Timmins, where they enjoyed "the best entertainers in Ontario," according to the *Porcupine Advance*, the newspaper of the day.

Early the next morning the trains began an hourly service to the Big Dome where citizens and visitors alike were invited to tour both the surface and the underground workings and to watch the new 40-stamp mill turn out real gold bricks.

It was indeed a sensational show. The final event of the day is eloquently reported by the *Porcupine Advance*:

At 7:30 the banquet proceeded in the Majestic Theatre . . . the floral decorations were supplied by Dunlop and Company of Toronto, with the exception of the potted plants which came from the T. & N.O. observatory at Englehart. The tables were

"DOME" WATER TANK
IN WHICH 57 LIVES WERE SAVED
IN THE PORCUPINE FIRE
(THE FAMILY BATH-TUB)

The Dome compressor cooling water pond, in which 57 lives were saved from the fire. (top)

A new mill swiftly rises from the wreckage of the fire (November 1911). (centre)

South Porcupine, a tent city on the flame-swept ruins, summer 1911. (below)

SOUTH PORCUPINE
ARISING FROM ITS ASHES

very artistically arranged by the caterer, W. Prestwich, formerly of the Toronto Club, who, with his staff of 30 experienced
waiters, served the following menu with remarkable prompt-
ness, and in a most cheerful and satisfactory manner to all those
assembled:

Caviar

Clear Green Turtle Soup

Olives   Celery   Salted Nuts

Sweetbreads and Mushrooms
sous Cloche

Saddle of Lamb   Currant Jelly
New Potatoes   Green Beans

Nesselrode Pudding
Fancy Cakes   Hot House Grapes

Nuts   Raisins   Coffee

The speeches continued far into the night, but there is no
mention made of champagne toasts on this occasion, and one
wonders if the guests had to contend with the legendary South
Porcupine water.

Dome was commended by J.C. Murray, editor of the *Canadian Mining
Journal*, for its quick action and its insistence upon building fireproof structures in the future. He also noted that throughout the Porcupine camp rebuilding was occurring with all haste. "Next year hardly a trace of the havoc wrought
will remain. The way of the prospector has been made easier. Large areas,
almost impassable for the prospector before the fire, have been cleared." This
did, indeed, prove advantageous for Dome, resulting in one spectacular find
which was described, almost lyrically, in the *Canadian Mining Journal*:

> What is considered by some engineers to be one of the most
> spectacular showings ever found in any camp is the rich vein
> uncovered on the eastern portion of the big Dome property
> recently. While trenching north and south, a beautiful free gold
> showing was uncovered on a vein running east and west for 72
> feet, and eight distinct spectacular showings were disclosed . . .
> The show spot of the vein is a patch of almost solid gold 2-½
> inches by 15 inches. In each case the gold appeared in slabs of
> schist in the quartz veins, 18 feet to 20 feet in width.

The "Golden Sidewalk," as it was called, a sensational display of natural
treasure, was matched in brilliance and value only by the original Jack Wilson-

Harry Preston discovery just over a year earlier. The news of the discovery spread beyond the Porcupine district and Dome Mines' stock "perked up," as Clary Dixon put it. "I know it did," he said ruefully. "I bought some Dome shares at 50 cents and sold them at $3 because I needed the money to pay for a couple of years of study at university. You could say it was a rather expensive education, because Dome kept going up until, in my time, it reached $40 and even more!"

The Golden Sidewalk proved to be a talisman as the Company strove for full production from the ore of a richly endowed property as the year 1912 dawned.

The Growing Pains of a New Mine

By the end of 1911, eight shafts had been sunk at Dome, reaching depths of 20 to 125 feet. Drifting and cross-cutting totalling 1,310 feet had been done at the 50-foot level and there had been a total of 9,064 feet of diamond drilling completed. However, there was still no guarantee that the glittering promise in the Golden Sidewalk and the Golden Stairway would go much below the surface. "Dome is a freak — it's a conglomerate; it will pinch out," skeptics prophesied. The retiring President certainly thought otherwise. W.S. Edwards, although not himself a mining expert, preferred to trust the judgment of such knowledgeable people as John S. Wilson, prospector and fellow Director; H.E. Meek, the General Superintendent; W.W. Mein, Consulting Engineer; and Henry Hanson, Mill Superintendent. The counsel of these men undoubtedly backed Edwards' optimistic summary at the start of 1912:

> The diamond drill work indicated a large body of ore of good mill value, and such ore has been cut at various depths to a thousand feet. It will be necessary to do a large amount of sinking and drifting in this orebody before it will be possible to state intelligently its size, and what will be the average values of the ore to be milled. However, sufficient work has been done to justify the management in equipping the property with the most permanent type of buildings and machinery, with the view to extending the plant as the further development of the mine may warrant.

The overall direction of mining operations, including the rebuilding of the devastated plant, was the responsibility of H.E. Meek. Originally from Michigan, Meek had moved to Dome from Copper Cliff and was highly regarded in the mining world. The *Cobalt Nugget* called him "benevolent, assiduous, and enterprising," and when he left Dome in 1914 to go to California, his fellow workers thought so highly of him that they presented him with a chest of silver at a banquet held in his honour.

Dome luckily escaped the misfortune that befell one of its neighbours in 1912. That summer there had been threatening bush fires to the west of the Dome property, and one mine which lay in the path of the creeping flames was the Foley O'Brien. The mine's manager was Bill Hatch, a geologist who had opened the first assay office in South Porcupine. An internationally recognized authority and world champion of bridge, Hatch was also an outstanding athlete who had once played baseball for the New York Giants.

The bush fire had been burning for several days and the sports enthusiasts among the workers at the various mines in the camp were not inclined to allow such a minor disturbance to interfere with their pastimes. Fire or no fire, the game between the South Porcupine baseball club and the Foley O'Brien team began on time at a diamond a few hundred feet from the mine buildings.

Hatch was at bat and the score was 2-2. As he took a swing at the ball, he noticed that one of the mine buildings was afire. His first thought was to drop the bat and race to the scene of the fire, but he reconsidered. He had wagered $600 on the game and the score was tied. Should he abandon the game and perhaps lose it and his $600, or stay?

"It was a tough spot to be in," he said later. "But I calculated that $600 was three months' salary, and there were more jobs to be had. I turned so that I wouldn't have to watch the mine burn down, and I scored the hit that won the game for Foley O'Brien."

Aside from the troubles caused by the 1911 fire, the first real problem to hit the mining camp came from an unexpected quarter. In the fall of 1912, with the backing of the powerful "One Big Union," a thousand miners went on strike, protesting the decision of a conciliation board which upheld the companies' right to cut wages in order to reduce rising costs. Under revolutionary banners, men of Hollinger, McIntyre, McEnaney, Vipond, Jupitor and Plenaurum mines paraded through the streets of the new town of Timmins.

At times the dispute became violent. Pitched battles took place between the strikers and the trainloads of strike breakers brought in by the mines, as well as the armed guards hired to protect them. Several men were shot, but fortunately no fatalities occurred. In a melée at South Porcupine, a revolver was reportedly shoved into a municipal official's stomach and the trigger pulled. The hammer clicked on the shell but did not fire.

Incidents of arson were also reported; one particularly ugly example involved the home of a Hollinger shift boss. Some mines set up their own police forces, which were reportedly armed. Despite the seething tension in the camp, Dome workers were among the last to go on strike, joining their colleagues in November.

Although tempers ran high for a few months, peace soon returned to the mines as differences were resolved. The effect of the strike on Dome could not have been great, for Monell's report at the end of 1912 stated that "production was well maintained in spite of the strike."

During the first few years of Dome's corporate life there was no expansion of its property holdings, except for the acquisition in 1912 of a four-mile right-of-way, which is still vital to the mine, for the installation of a water main and an electric pole line between the mine and Porcupine Lake. Two four-stage tur-bine pumps were installed at the lake to provide water to the plant, mainly for milling purposes. The new treatment plant, replacing the one lost in the 1911 fire, had a monthly capacity of 10,000 tons and by the end of March, 1913, had treated 101,812 tons.

Excessive costs were a matter of concern. Mein reported that operating costs for January 3, 1912, to March 31, 1913 (the Company having changed to a fiscal year), averaged $4.95 a ton milled, excluding development costs. That was high, he admitted, but would be "gradually and substantially reduced." Ambrose Monell confirmed this view in a reassuring address to shareholders. "This high cost was to be expected . . . (and) is particularly true starting in a new and undeveloped country, where good labour is hard to get in quantity. Working expenses, varying for gold mines in different parts of the continent from $2 to $10 per ton, are largely a function of the district in which the mines occur." He, like Mein, expected a decrease in operating expenses with the projected completion in February, 1913, of a hydro-electric power line from Wawaitin Falls, 13 miles away. By the end of March, only one shaft, No. 2, was still operating by steam power and that would soon be converted.

Dome, Monell happily reported, had a working profit of $509,996 since the fire, and ore reserves of 566,000 tons had been developed — "practically five years' supply for our present mill. Moreover, the existence of much greater bodies of ore has been proved by bore holes and by development at the 260-foot level of No. 2 shaft, to the east of Dome."

At a special meeting held early in 1914, the shareholders approved an increase of authorized capital from $3.5 million to $5 million. They were told, however, that "all expenditures for additions to the plant (which included increasing the mill's capacity to 28,000 tons a month, at a cost of $303,999) were met by profits from current operations, so that it has not been deemed necessary to issue any of these new shares."

Meek reported on the doubling of the mill to 80 stamps and the addition of five tube mills. He also noted that relations with the Company's employees had been "considerably better," that there was a "good supply of labour for all work," and that greater efficiency had been attained in all classes of work.

Costs had been lowered by $1.49 to $3.08 per ton of ore milled, "due to the use of hydro-electric power during most of the year, a larger tonnage milled, increased efficiency of methods, and a better supply of labour . . . (and) will be further reduced, and should be less than $2.50 per ton when the enlarged plant is in operation," Mein said. A year later, under a new President and management team, operating costs were again much lower, although they did not drop to Mein's predicted level, mostly because of the outbreak of war in Europe.

The year 1915, Dome's fifth anniversary as a corporation and its sixth as a mining property, was a memorable one for the Company. Ambrose Monell retired from Dome's activities to devote his time to the presidency of the International Nickel Company of New Jersey, and was replaced by Captain Joseph R. de la Mar, one of the original organizers of International Nickel. E.C. Converse and Charles Denison also retired, and the three Directors were succeeded by G.C. Miller and R.W. Pomeroy, both of Buffalo, New York, and Dr. T.N. Jamieson, who had returned after a brief absence. There was a change in management as well: Edwards continued on the Board and was First Vice-President, C.D. Kaeding replaced H.E. Meek in the capacity of Second Vice-President and General Manager, while H.P. DePencier, Kaeding's assistant, became Third Vice-President.

De la Mar immediately announced an offering of 50,000 treasury shares to create a fund "for the vigorous prosecution of development work; to determine as quickly as possible the tonnage of ore that may be treated profitably, and to subsequently increase the milling capacity commensurate with the extent of the ore so developed."

Operating costs in 1914-15 were down by $1.23 to $2.97 a ton, which de la Mar thought noteworthy as this had been attained despite "abnormal conditions due to the European war . . . and that the plant has not yet reached its estimated duty by 5,000 tons a month." Steps quickly taken by Kaeding to reduce costs and to increase efficiency included replacing the 16-cubic-foot ore cars with cars of 93-cubic-foot capacity; underground ore chutes were widened to accommodate the larger side-dump cars, and, since the ore crushers were oversize, a large bin in the rock house would now permit the crushing plant to operate on one shift instead of two per 24 hours. These changes cut the costs of haulage, crushing, and conveying by 50 per cent.

Kaeding, who, like Meek and Lawson before him, had moved to Dome from Copper Cliff, arrived with a reputation for efficiency, but was fair and reasonable in his assessment of what was a just charge to the Company. He pointed out that one reason costs had not been reduced as much as had been hoped for was due to the additional burden of the provincial Workmen's Compensation levy which came in force at the beginning of 1915. However, it was "an added tax which was welcomed, as it placed upon a sound and equitable basis the distribution of compensation for injuries sustained at work."

In 1915, the intricate pattern of the orebodies was finally worked out. Instead of mining in very large shrinkage stopes where dilution (the unavoidable removal of waste or low-grade rock along with the ore) was a factor, more selective stoping resulted in an improvement in grade of ore treated. An ore reserve calculation showed that, although almost 800,000 tons of low-grade material had been eliminated, the reserve tonnage was reduced only 200,000 tons to 2,600,000, while the grade was increased from $4.15 to $6.20 per ton, based on gold at $20.67 per ounce.

About this time the tonnage of 800 tons per day had become too large for the No. 2 shaft, which passed through ore now required for mining. Accordingly, shaft No. 3, a five-compartment shaft with a single deck cage capable of holding 40 men or five tons of material, was commenced in late 1915. It is a tribute to Kaeding, its designer, that today it is still serving the upper part of the mine. The savings which have accrued over the years as a result of operating only one main shaft from surface cannot be determined but must be very large. It is also worth noting that at depth a good deal of ore is contained in its pillar.

Dome Mines Company Limited ended the fiscal year of 1914-15 with an operating profit of $315,179. At the Annual Meeting in Toronto, de la Mar dropped the first hint of dividends:

> We have an orebody of great length and width and fair values,
> and the old rule still holds good in mining — that when you
> cannot pay dividends from quality, you may from quantity, if
> the ore holds out. My 40 years of mining experience tell me that
> it will hold out for very many years.

On June 23, 1915, the shares of Dome Mines Company Limited were listed on the New York Stock Exchange. By that time $500,000 had been raised from the sale of the 50,000 treasury shares, of which $318,019 was used for construction work and additional development. Soon after the start of trading in Dome shares, de la Mar made an important announcement:

> In July, the Company, having reached a strong position where
> continuous earnings were assured, a quarterly dividend was
> established, and the first dividend of five per cent, $200,000,
> was paid on September 1, 1915. Three dividends, or a total of
> $600,000, were paid during the financial year.

By March 31, 1916, current assets of the Company exceeded current liabilities by $871,625. Operating costs had been lowered by 43.5 cents a ton — not as much as in previous years, but a creditable amount for a wartime period. Dome's underground workings were now moving close to its eastern neighbour, Dome Extension Mines Company Limited.

A typical shaft station during
sinking of No. 3 shaft in 1916.
(above)

Dome Extension property and
buildings in 1915. (below)

CHAPTER 6

The Dome Extension

When he declared Dome's first dividend, de la Mar also announced that the Company was expanding its operation for the first time by taking an option on the adjacent claims of Dome Extension Mines Company Limited. After just one year of war in Europe, Dome was feeling its effects and only sound management would enable the Company to maintain adequate profitability. It made sense, then, that Dome should look to its neighbour for further growth opportunities.

The Dome Extension mine consisted of five claims in Tisdale Township and formed part of the group staked by Jack Wilson and his companions in 1909, which, because they did not appear to have the potential of the Big Dome, were not included in the purchase effected from W.S. Edwards. The property was operated by Dome Extension Mines Company Limited, incorporated in January, 1911, with Edwards who, as President, held 1.5 million shares of the 2.0 million share capital stock of the company. Edwards, therefore, was a Director both of Dome Extension and of Dome, as was Alexander Fasken, Secretary of both the smaller company and Dome, and who would hold similar positions at Dome for nearly thirty-four years. The Mine Superintendent at Dome Extension was "Captain" H.C. Anchor, a legendary figure among the colourful mining men of the area early in the twentieth century.

De la Mar explained Dome's plan regarding the Extension:

> . . . We have secured an 18-months' option on all of the property . . . and propose to diligently develop this and also the 800 to 1,000 feet of ground lying between our present workings and that property. This ground is known to contain ore within a short distance of the dividing line.
>
> If our principal orebody continues to this dividing line, it will pass into the Dome Extension ground at a depth of 900 to 1,000 feet and can be economically developed from our lower levels. Besides the fair prospects of a continuation of our ore into the

Dome Extension, that company is now developing a body of five dollar ore within 200 feet of the surface, indicating a continuation of the mineral-bearing zone within the Dome Extension lines.

Commenting on de la Mar's announcement, the *Canadian Mining Journal* told its readers that the option "appears to be a clear-cut agreement upon which there should be little argument, and it should be for the benefit of both companies." It then gave more details:

> The Dome takes an option of the total assets of the Dome Extension Mines for the sum of $1,150,000 to be paid for by the issue . . . of Dome shares. The option is open until October 15, 1917. Under this option the Dome Mines must sink their shaft to a depth of 850 feet and carry a drift at 800 feet into the territory of Dome Extension . . . Not less than an average of 100 feet of drifting should be done . . . every month and that not less than $3,000 should be so spent. At the same time the Dome Extension may proceed with any work they may see fit as long as they do not interfere with the Dome development.
>
> . . . It is believed by everyone in the camp that the orebody found on the Big Dome dips into the Dome Extension at a depth of 1,200 feet or thereabouts, and in this case the development of their part of the property should show some very valuable ore.

The Company began to feel pressures of the conflict overseas. In 1916, operating costs increased by 14 cents a ton although average costs per ounce of gold recovered declined by 39 cents. As well, as a result of extensions to the plant, Dome now had a milling capacity of 45,000 tons per month and the capacity to mine more than twice that amount. The plant extension and the expanded development programmes had used up all of the $500,000 realized from the sale of Dome shares and another $229,000 from earnings. One saving was realized by cutting the 1917 dividend from 50 to 25 cents a share, because of the "unsatisfactory labour conditions prevailing in the Porcupine district," de la Mar explained at the Annual Meeting. Of the 2,300 men normally employed in the camp's mines, 600 had enlisted by mid-1916 and many others were attracted to the Cobalt silver mines and the copper mines in the United States, which were offering bonuses made possible by the sharp rise in the prices of silver and copper. Nevertheless, de la Mar continued to be optimistic that these problems would be overcome. Dome, he confidently affirmed, was "a long-lived mine with liberal orebodies which will be profitably mined for many years to come, and the labour shortage will eventually rectify itself."

C.D. Kaeding placed the blame squarely on "agitators and organizers" who were stirring up trouble, "especially among the aliens." "There is no longer any efficiency among the mine workmen, and the ones still remaining with us are working intermittently and half-heartedly," he charged. Bonuses were paid in order to entice more industrious workers. Assistance was also given indirectly by keeping the price of a meal in the Company boarding houses at 25 cents — the price charged in 1912 — although each meal cost the Company 31 cents. In total, the boarding houses, bunkhouses, dormitories, dwellings, staff hospital and the Company store operated at an annual loss of nearly $45,000. Despite these efforts, by the fall of 1917 Dome's work force was only 60 per cent of the number required to operate properly and on December 1 the mill was shut down. Production did not resume until a year and a half later, in June, 1919.

The financial condition of the Company was still good, however. In mid-1917, cash, supplies and other current assets exceeded current liabilities by $601,000. If the mill had to be closed, it was reassuring to have a nest egg to fall back on.

Taking advantage of the shutdown, Kaeding had "all the good men obtainable" sink the main No. 3 shaft to 1,250 feet and drive a lateral drift to the boundary between Dome and Dome Extension. At 1,150 feet, the ore was reported as being "promising as to size and values." Proper ore and waste handling facilities were also installed. The shaft was later deepened to the 18th level at a vertical depth of 2,318 feet; ore and waste pockets and the main hoisting facilities were installed below the 16th level, and subsidiary hoisting facilities below the 18th level.

At the expiration of the Dome Extension option in October, 1917, the engineers and geologists, anxious to continue their work, sought and were given an extension of time. Jules S. Bache, elected president of Dome Mines after the death of de la Mar on December 1, 1918, described the renewed option in his first report to shareholders for the 1918 fiscal year:

> We have the option to purchase the property and assets of that company (Dome Extension) for 79,666 fully-paid shares of the capital stock. Your Company has no obligation, but, if it desires to keep the option in force, an average sum of $3,000 per month in exploration and development must be expended.

When the option expired again on March 15, 1920, it was extended for yet another six months, so hopeful were Dome's engineers that the years of development work were about to pay off. Two months after this renewal, H.P. DePencier, now General Manager, felt that all the work and expense had been justified. He announced that the diamond drill holes "indicate an orebody dipping north and raking eastward into the Dome Extension. The results already obtained in the development of this orebody at the 10th level in the Dome within a short distance of the Dome Extension are such as to lead us to confidently anticipate that a very considerable profit will be won ... when development to lower levels has been accomplished." Dome Extension's future looked so bright to the cautious DePencier that he did not hesitate to recommend the purchase to the shareholders and, at a special meeting held on September 14, 1920, the option was taken up. To one interested observer, this action was wise. R.E. Hore, editor of the *Canadian Mining Journal*, commented:

> The exercising of the option ... by Dome Mines is generally regarded as a very important step forward in the making of a great mine at the Dome. The resources of the companies being now combined, the development of the Dome Extension property at depth is assured. It is understood that the purchase ... greatly increases the possibilities of a long and profitable life for the Dome.

By the end of the 1920 fiscal year, over two and a half years after the Armistice ending the war, Dome Mines was financially healthier than it had been at any time since 1915, when the first dividends were paid. Conditions were so good that the Company resumed payment of dividends — four of them, in fact. Nevertheless, operations that year had been difficult due to a shortage of men for underground work during the early months and a subsequent insufficiency of electric power. However, Bache reported that both situations had been rectified by May, 1921. As the prices of supplies slowly declined, the scale of operations moved upwards to the milling of 1,000 tons a day, prompting the President to state with justifiable pride, "We therefore look forward to a year of great prosperity."

CHAPTER 7

Flashback: Monell and de la Mar

In the first eighteen years of its corporate existence, Dome Mines Company Limited had four Presidents, the first of whom was John Francis Hope McCarthy. A Toronto lawyer and one of the five shareholders who had elected themselves provisional directors at the first general meeting of shareholders, he was elected President at 9:15 a.m. on April 12, 1910, and at 4:00 p.m. was succeeded by William S. Edwards, the grubstaker of the prospecting expedition that led to the discovery of the Dome. Since J.F.H. McCarthy's presidency was a *pro tem* appointment, Edwards was the first "working" President. But this was also short-lived. The minutes of the Annual General Meeting held on January 4, 1911, said:

> The President reported to the meeting that under the terms of the agreement entered into between Ambrose Monell and the then owners of the mining properties owned by the Company all work being done on the Company's properties is being done by the said Ambrose Monell at his own expense as provided in the said agreement, and that the Company has not, up to date, received any moneys or disbursed any moneys.

On March 22, 1911, the Directors (W.S. Edwards, Ambrose Monell, Alexander Fasken, George H. Sedgwick, and A.T. Struthers), elected Monell Vice-President and appointed him "General Manager of the Company with full charge of all the Company's operations at the Mine." Statements later submitted by Monell to the Board showed that, since March, 1910, he and his associates had spent $250,000 on the Dome mill and $125,000 on development and exploration work.

Beginning in 1912, Ambrose Monell exercised, on behalf of Dome, the administrative skills which had advanced him to the presidency of International Nickel in 1902, at the age of twenty-eight. Monell and his successor at Dome, Joseph de la Mar, both strong men of ambition, vigour and natural talent, were in command during the period when firm leadership was essential for the company's survival.

Ambrose Monell was born in New York in 1873. His father was a lawyer and a judge and had hoped that his son would be the fourth generation of the Monells to practice law. Ambrose, however, wanted no part of the legal profession and became interested instead in metallurgy, deciding to enter the School of Mines at Columbia University.

After graduation in 1896 he obtained a job with the Carnegie Steel Company in Pittsburgh through the personal interest of the great Andrew Carnegie himself. He had met the founder of the vast Carnegie enterprise through George Whitfield, a fellow student at Columbia and brother-in-law of Carnegie. When the Carnegies asked Whitfield to visit them for some fishing in Andrew Carnegie's native Scotland, Monell was included in the invitation.

Monell, a master in the arts of angling and hunting since his boyhood, was "brought up with a rod in one hand and a gun in the other." In fact, *The Salmon and the Dry Fly*, written as a tribute to Monell by George M.L. LaBranche, described him as "the first angler in this country to take a salmon on a dry fly . . . As a salmon angler he was unequalled." Monell went fishing with Carnegie and, after catching more salmon than anyone else, offered to give his host a demonstration. The next day Carnegie had greater success, thanks to Monell's tutoring. Monell told Carnegie about his studies at Columbia, of his plans for becoming a metallurgical engineer, and his hopes of finding employment that would involve him in metals. "When you finish," said Carnegie, "come and see me. I'll see if I can find something for you." Monell, in due course, called on Carnegie and was hired.

Monell set to work redesigning the ports of the open hearth furnaces in the steel mills, resulting in large fuel savings and reduced costs. Carnegie praised Monell, now regarded as one of his "bright young men," and gave him a bonus of $25,000.

Young Monell soon rose to the position of Chief Metallurgist in the steel company, where he attracted the attention of the fledgling International Nickel Company and accepted the offered position of President. *The Saturday Evening Post* reported that Monell was now paid an annual salary of $20,000 as well as a share of the International Nickel profits, which, the magazine said, would add $40,000 to his income.

As operating head of International Nickel Monell travelled frequently to Canada to oversee the proper running of the mines and mills in the Sudbury Basin. He was not pleased with the Canadian operations and was determined to change them. In his first report to International Nickel shareholders in 1903, he complained that the smelting plant at Sudbury was "badly located," the furnaces were "small and costly to operate," the locomotives and cars were

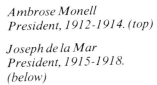

Ambrose Monell
President, 1912-1914. (top)

Joseph de la Mar
President, 1915-1918.
(below)

"old, inadequate and practically worthless," and there was "a total lack of machinery for handling ores and materials economically."

Although Edwards bore the title of President when Monell first turned his managerial eye on the Dome property, Monell was very much in command. Since he was paying the bills, he made sure that he received value for his money and from the start used experts in mining and management from his Sudbury operation.

The book *Nickel: An Historical Review* says that Ambrose Monell "was a man of strong and decisive character, but had a pleasant, approachable, and well-balanced personality." During his visit to the Dome soon after the fire, Monell learned that a local merchant was charging exhorbitant prices for his goods, enraging the survivors. "Monell," said K.P. Bernhard, one of Dome's accountants, "went to the merchant and asked him what his entire stock was worth, paid him the asking price, and had the goods distributed to the needy without charge."

Monell was by first choice a metallurgist and the inventor of the stainless steel alloy that bore his name — monell metal, shortened in later years to monel metal. Dome was in expert hands with such a creative man in command during its formative years.

With the outbreak of war in 1914, Monell found that his time and energy were being increasingly taken up with International Nickel, whose product was in growing demand for the making of munitions and armaments. Monell gave so much of his time to the Sudbury Basin and to Bayonne, N.J., that Dome was bound to suffer. Realizing this, he resigned from the Board of Dome in 1915, gave up the position of President, and sold his Dome stock to Joseph de la Mar. When the United States entered the war in 1917, Monell gave up the presidency of International Nickel, joined the American Army with the rank of colonel, and served in the Signal Corps with distinction. At war's end he became active in politics and campaigned, unsuccessfully, to help General Leonard Wood win the Republican nomination for the U.S. presidency.

In the autumn of 1918 Monell became gravely ill. Despite every possible medical attention, in May 1921 death came to the man who had headed the struggling Dome Mines Company Limited. He was 48 years old.

Ambrose Monell left his colleagues at Dome a company that had weathered the perils which beset every young corporation, as well as the catastrophic fire and the effects of worldwide conflict. Monell turned over to de la Mar a gold mining company of "the highest standard of metallurgical and economic efficiency."

Joseph de la Mar was the son of Maximilian de la Mar and the grandson of a Parisian banker. Maximilian operated one of the bank's branches in Amsterdam, and married a Dutch woman of German descent. They became the parents of Joseph Raphael (Maximilian was an art afficionado) in 1843. Maximilian de la Mar lived only six years after the birth of his son. His sudden death threw the household into a turmoil, so upsetting the child that he ran away from home and stowed away on a Dutch ship bound for the East Indies. Upon being discovered he was put to work as an unpaid dishwasher and general helper for the ship's cook to earn his passage. He won the hearts of the crew and did such a good job that on the return voyage he was paid the equivalent of forty cents a month.

Upon his return to Amsterdam, young Joseph went back to his family. He had fallen in love with life at sea, but even in those days of child labour the age of seven was far too young to become a sailor. In due course he did become a seaman with a strong ambition to command his own ship. He began giving himself a general education by reading whatever books he could lay his hands on and learned navigation from *Navigator's Epitome*, the only textbook on the subject available to him. When he was 20 he obtained his certificate as a master mariner and was given command of his own ship three years later.

The neophyte sea captain soon became frustrated, seeing no future in seafaring. After crossing the Atlantic, he went into business as a diver at Vineyard Haven, an island off the north shore of Martha's Vineyard. He became a submarine contractor who, for a price, raised sunken ships. However, after hoisting 41 ships from the coastal waters, his interest waned.

Then, a new chance for adventure beckoned. Gold was discovered in Colorado in the seventies and scores of eager fortune-seekers headed for the western states, Joseph de la Mar among them. He eventually found potentially good land at Leadville, Colorado, and near Silver City, Idaho. With an associate, Colonel Dewey, he acquired rights to many of the old silver and gold claims and then went to Chicago, where he spent some time studying metallurgy and chemistry. Two years later, the Leadville property was sold for $2 million and the Idaho properties became the De Lamar Mine.

In the 1890s the town of De Lamar sprang up close to the mine, which was sold to a London mining company and continued to operate until manpower shortages brought about by the First World War forced its closing. More than half a century later, with new technology and rising precious metal prices, the mine was reopened. It is now known as the De Lamar Silver Mine and continues as a low-cost producer of silver and gold bullion.

From 1888 until his death in 1918 at the age of 70, de la Mar spent most of his time in New York, with some time off for sojourns in Paris, where he became a speculator and investor in many successful business ventures.

In business relations, de la Mar was "extremely taciturn and aloof," according to the *Dictionary of American Biography*, although these characteristics were not evident in his Canadian dealings. In his personal relationships he was gregarious and amiable, entertaining extravagantly in magnificent mansions where even the wealthiest of his guests was soon in awe.

In the late 1880s, at Oak Bluffs, on the island of Martha's Vineyard, de la Mar met Nellie Sands, a druggist's daughter, and was so dazzled by her beauty and her red bathing suit that he married her and settled $500,000 on her. He built a splendid house for her on Madison Avenue in New York, handing the workmen cigars wrapped in five dollar bills as incentives to speed up its construction. Some years later, when the family vacated the mansion, it became the home of the National Democratic Club, and a favourite haunt of Tammany Hall.

From New York Mr. and Mrs. de la Mar moved to Paris, where one of their temporary homes was a palace on the Avenue du Bois de Boulogne. They entertained lavishly, and Mrs. de la Mar was persuaded to have her portrait painted by a prominent French artist. She was hailed by one newspaper as one of the "world's four most beautiful women." (The other three were said to be the Tsarina of Russia, Vera Boardman, and Princess Henry of Pless.) This distinction did not, however, save her from her husband's wrath when he found purportedly incriminating letters in her desk. He sued for and was granted a divorce. "The decree was issued five years to the day, to the hour, to the minute, after their marriage, a coincidence which made a deep impression on the Captain," the *New Yorker* reported.

Like his father, de la Mar was fond of good works of art, and was skilled at both the piano and the organ. One of the treasures which the Democrats acquired with the Madison Avenue mansion was a gilded Steinway piano.

De la Mar left an estate of $20 million, a satisfying amount in view of his extravagant style of living. Half of this amount was bequeathed to his only child, Alice Antoinette, who never married, and the rest was divided equally between the medical schools of Columbia, Harvard and Johns Hopkins Universities.

CHAPTER 8

Mining in the Booming Twenties

As Dome Mines took over Dome Extension and a new decade began, Jules S. Bache had been at the Dome helm for a year and would remain there for nearly a quarter of a century. It was the hand of a banker which guided Dome with skill through the prosperous yet turbulent years leading up to the economic depression of the thirties.

During Ambrose Monell's presidency, the position of Treasurer had been held by James L. Ashley, but when Joseph de la Mar became President he also retained the post of Treasurer, as did Jules Bache when he assumed the leadership of Dome.

A number of Dome Mines Company shares were part of de la Mar's estate. Bache had heard rumours that these shares could well become highly profitable and purchased them, becoming Dome's largest shareholder. At this time, however, Dome was not a very promising investment. The First World War had just ended and the mine had not been in production for 18 months.

The new President was well equipped by ability, background, experience and personality to conduct Dome's affairs in the difficult post-war years. Born in New York in 1861, he began his career as a cashier at the age of 19 in the firm of Leopold Cahn and Company, investment bankers and brokers. Cahn, Bache's uncle, had founded the company in 1879. Bache became its treasurer soon after being hired and three years later a partner. In 1892 Leopold Cahn and Company was reorganized under the name of J.S. Bache and Company, attracting as clients such financial giants as John D. Rockefeller Sr., Edward H. Harriman and Jay Gould. In the twenties the firm was a leader in the financing of railways and automobiles. J.S. Bache and Company evolved into the Bache Group then Bache, Halsey, Stuart and Shields Incorporated and finally became Prudential-Bache Securities.

Having acquired a major interest in Dome, Bache asked officials of the Ontario Bureau of Mines for their opinion of the property. To his amazement, they told him that there was little hope of a real gold mine being developed in the province and that he would be wasting his time and money if he proceeded. Bache refused to accept this pessimistic view. "The Bureau of Mines was wrong and should be shaken up and ordered to carry out a realistic examination of the gold mining situation," he told friends.

One of these friends, Col. John Bayne MacLean, founder of the MacLean Publishing Company which eventually became Maclean-Hunter, passed Bache's comments on to Premier E.C. Drury. Drury instructed the Bureau to make a thorough study of gold mining in the province, which resulted in a report that was completely at variance with the previously gloomy opinion held by its senior staff.

During Bache's first full year in the presidency many problems had to be faced, the most serious of which was the shortage of workers. C.D. Kaeding said: "The scarcity of labour has seriously hampered the operation and is the cause of grave concern." With the return of peace, many foreign-born employees had returned to their native lands, and others had been attracted to better paying jobs offered by the burgeoning manufacturing plants. Producers of gold from low-grade ore, like Dome, were severely handicapped in the competition for "satisfactory labour, even in insufficient numbers," Kaeding added. It was at this time that Dome began recruiting experienced tin miners from England, mainly from the Camborne and Redruth districts of Cornwall. Several groups of these "Cousin Jacks" emigrated to Canada and settled in the Porcupine district, thirty of them finding immediate employment at Dome. A welcome and stabilizing influence on the labour scene, many third-generation descendants of these families are still employed at the mine.

In 1920, H.P. DePencier succeeded Kaeding, who left to become a consulting mining engineer. DePencier had to face a variety of problems over the next few years, beginning with a shortage of men for underground work. This had no sooner been alleviated when Dome was forced to return to more expensive steam power as sufficient electrical power to carry out its planned extension could not be obtained until a hydro-electric plant at Sturgeon Falls was completed. Delays in construction and abnormally low rainfall aggravated the situation, compelling Dome to reduce milling operations until late 1923. High freight rates and taxes, and the inflated cost of supplies as compared to pre-war times began to take their toll on profits as well. Price increases experienced since 1914 were: detonators, 152 per cent; fuses, 111 per cent; soft coal, 57 per cent; fuel oil, 30 per cent; and lumber, 78 per cent.

In 1923, Dome Mines Company Limited became Dome Mines Limited, and W.S. Edwards, the Dome grubstaker who had been First Vice-President since 1912, relinquished his position but continued as an active Board member until his death three years later.

Merrill filter presses, inside
the mill. (top)

No. 6 winze, underground hoist
room, at 16th level. (centre)

No. 6 winze, (underground
shaft) 16th level (depth 2,200
feet). (below)

Once labour and power conditions had returned to normal, Dome was able to bounce back quickly for the remainder of 1923. Business was so good that the outgoing Dome Mines Company Limited paid two dividends of $1 each, and the young Dome Mines Limited paid its first dividend of 50 cents a share, all in the same year. This prosperity continued into the middle of the decade, and *The Northern Miner* commented:

> Dome has been a wonderful dividend performer . . . Dome's dividends are approximately two-thirds of Hollinger's on one-third the production. That's a splendid showing for Dome. The Northern Miner believes it voices Northern feeling when it says that the General Manager, his assistants, and the whole Dome crew have done wonderfully well with the ticklish problems presented by one of the most unusual gold mines in the world, and one with an irregularity of ore occurrences and a peculiarity of geology that would drive most engineers white-haired.

In the summer of 1925, a winze, or underground shaft, was sunk from the 13th level 1,608 feet east of the main shaft. A total of 281 feet was advanced between the first and the last days of August, through the efforts of three shifts of six men each, excavating a total of 2,150 tons of rock. It was "splendid work," said the *Miner*, setting "a sinking record for the North country and . . . perhaps a metal mine record for Canada."

Meanwhile, Dome exploration staff were seeking new opportunities farther afield. Properties in Quebec were examined but attention was soon diverted to more promising areas in the Red Lake district of northwestern Ontario. Dome took an option on the Howey property in 1925. A partial exposure of mineralized rock 930 feet long attracted closer scrutiny and in the following year 18 diamond drill holes were drilled to an aggregate depth of 7,335 feet. However, in the opinion of the General Manager, these results did not justify further development and the option was dropped.

A more detailed account of the Howey-Dome story is given by Arnold Hoffman, in his book *Free Gold: The Story of Canadian Mining*, published in 1947. Apparently, Douglas Wright, Dome's chief geologist, had persuaded his Company to take the option on the property held by the Howey Gold Mine Syndicate and Jack Hammell, who was associated with exciting discoveries at Flin Flon, Manitoba. He was one of the pioneers in the use of aircraft in the development of remote mining properties. Ore occurrences of interest had been found on the shore of Red Lake by two brothers, Lorne and Ray Howey. Dome carried out trenching and drilling in the early winter of 1926 which produced results that Wright regarded as favourable. However, DePencier was "in violent disagreement," and when the option was dropped, Wright "angrily resigned" and signed up with Jack Hammell, who took over the Howey stock which had been granted to Dome for expenses.

The decision to drop the Howey option may have been one of the few errors DePencier made in a long and successful career, but it was made when gold was $20.67 per ounce. With the backing of the remarkable Jack Hammell and the fortuitous increase in the price of gold to $35 per ounce in 1934, the Howey mine, after a few years of difficulties, began to pay. Until its ore was exhausted in 1941, the Howey produced $13,167,134 in gold and paid $2,150,000 in dividends. Henry Hanson, Dome's first Mill Superintendent, recalls that "these dividends did not make anyone wealthy, but the mine did inspire more intense prospecting and more profitable ventures."

The mode of transportation available to the prospectors of seven decades ago was a far cry from today's sophisticated mechanical workhorses. The silent paddling of rugged canoeists has been replaced by the dull roar of motorboats and the deep-throated throb of airplanes and helicopters, which, although much more efficient, seem not to hold the same romantic air of adventure. One major innovation which has definitely benefited from modern technology, though, is the snowmobile.

Now widely used for recreational and, to a lesser extent, commercial travel in northern Ontario, and a familiar sight to both city and bush dwellers, our present-day snowmobile had as its roots a number of weird and wonderful machines. One of the first "snowmobiles" ever used was a contraption powered by two horizontal cylinders which were separated by a helical screw drive mechanism, the purpose of which was to bore through the snow thereby propelling the snowmobile forward. Capable of hauling six men and their gear through the bush, the machine came complete with Mac, its own experienced mechanic, when it was purchased jointly by Dome Mines and McIntyre Porcupine Mines in the late twenties. Its maiden voyage for the co-owners was to be the trek from Sioux Lookout to Red Lake, a distance of about 120 miles, carrying a party of Dome employees. Along for the ride was John "Turn 'Em Down" Reid, who, although very quiet and reserved in manner, was widely respected for his skills as a mining consultant.

After only ten miles, the machine bogged down in the soft, deep snow, apparently quite content to take a lengthy rest. The men, having naturally left their old-fashioned snowshoes behind, had to put up with three or four days of miserable living, spending most of their time berating poor Mac, who couldn't manage to get the newfangled and temperamental beast going again. After being subjected to much verbal abuse, he wearily turned to Reid, who had remained stoically silent throughout the barrage of insults, and asked him why he was being so quiet about the machine. Reid, a very proper gentleman at all

This was the type of early snowmobile, at left and right of photo, used by Dome and McIntyre in the Red Lake district in 1926.

times, looked Mac straight in the eye and quietly replied: "The trouble with the machine is that it's too big to be stuffed up you know where."

In 1927 C.W. Dowsett, General Superintendent of Dome for five years, resigned to take a position in South Africa, where he would have "greater opportunities for the exercise of his well-known metallurgical talents and experience," said DePencier. Replacing him was Joseph H. Stovel.

DePencier announced the intention of drilling 460 feet deeper into Dome Extension, into an area which corresponded geologically to one in Dome proper from which ore worth $4.5 million had been removed. "If," declared DePencier, "after we have sunk this shaft to 3,000 feet, we find nothing, I'm through." In 1928, DePencier was forced to confess that results had been "distinctly disappointing." Some shareholders accused the General Manager of being overly pessimistic, and that he was just too cautious and conservative. Not so, stoutly defended Bache. "DePencier refuses to promise you something he does not know anything about. As for the Dome Mine itself, that is a long way from fading out. The mine is good for another two years, might even be good for two more years after that . . . I am willing to make the statement again that it is my hope that we will still be mining gold when our children are growing up."

Dome continued to prosper well into 1929 but in October, for the second time in its brief history, the mill was destroyed by fire, caused this time by an overheated chimney stack in the adjacent boiler plant. The date coincided with the infamous stock market crash and Joe Stovel remembered that "when Jules Bache was advised that his pet investment, Dome Mines, was also in trouble, it did not add to his joy in life."

Winter was about to descend and DePencier was concerned about his employees' well-being. Obviously, without production and therefore without income, the Company could not keep a full complement of workers. However, married men were given first priority to carry out work that could be done in the meantime. This would ensure that a nucleus of employees would be maintained, around which a full work force could be built when the new mill came into operation. The first task, however, was to clear away the debris from which a total of $534,848 in bullion was recovered.

Dome, however, had yet to feel the bitter effects of depression which would gradually spread across the western world. Gold mines have traditionally continued to operate successfully in times of economic depression as they have no difficulty in selling their product, and labour becomes plentiful as other industries are forced to resort to lay-offs.

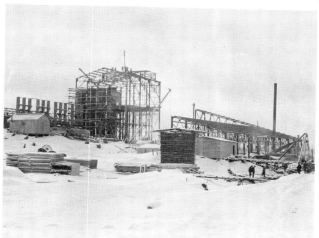

*The great mill structure
collapsed (top) and
damaged expensive
machinery (centre) during
the fire of 1929.*

*Restoration of ruined
buildings was well underway
by December of the same
year. (below)*

*Dome Directors at lunch
after inspecting the fire
damage at the property.
(Jules Bache sitting, second
from left). (above)*

*President Bache's private
railway car on Dome mine's
T. & N.O. siding. (below)*

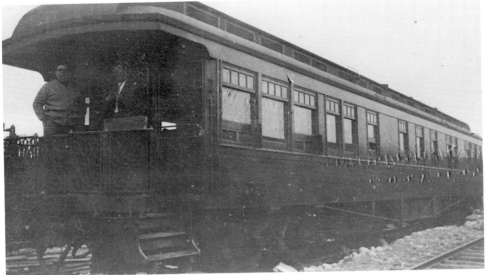

CHAPTER 9

The Depression Years

The year 1930 began badly for Dome Mines because of the earlier destruction of its mill, which was, fortunately, fully covered by insurance. "Yet," reported *The Northern Miner*, "during the twelve months when the Company had no mill, it practically broke even, with income from bullion recovered from the old plant and figuring on income from investment sources . . . Thus, although the Company had lost a year in time, it has been able to retain its strong treasury position."

The new mill operated close to its daily capacity of 1,500 tons during the last two months of 1930. Taking advantage of the rebuilding period, the crushing plant was remodelled and a new crusher installed. A 60,000-gallon water tank was erected and eight-inch water mains were laid for an automatic sprinkler system in both mill and crusher for fire protection.

Dome now began to venture into South African gold mining. Stocks held intermittently between 1937 and 1951, on which Dome broke about even, were: 28,400 shares of Grootvlei Proprietary Mines Limited, 21,000 shares of Venterspost Gold Mining Company Limited, and 7,415 shares of Blyvooruitzicht Gold Mining Company Limited. In 1930, Dome had also purchased 90,000 shares of East Geduld Mines Limited, a new mine in the famous Rand, for $1,106,802. "Operations and developments at East Geduld have fully met our expectations," said Bache. Geduld, however, had little to do with Dome's success during a difficult year of the depression. Dome stock dropped to $4.40 a share in 1929, a result of the fire and the crash of the stock market, but rose to between $7 and $8 before 1930 was over.

In 1933, Geduld paid two dividends, triple the amounts paid the year before. "Extremely satisfactory," pronounced Bache, who also reported the sale, at a profit, of part of Dome's holdings in the Geduld mine.

When the shareholders gathered for the Annual Meeting in May of that year, the President was beaming. "For the past five years, at these Annual Meetings,

The Dome mill, reconstructed after the 1929 fire. (above)

Press for a gold amalgam cake. (centre)

Amalgam cakes. (below)

I have been making references to the possibility of finding a new mine," said Bache. "Gentlemen, we can now say that we have a new rich mine on the Dome."

"H.P. DePencier, always cautious, always conservative about the future, was visibly excited," reported one journalist. The General Manager then made a statement that seemed so out of character that there could be no doubt about the good news: "We have sections of core with gold visible half the length of this room." The new mine was in the middle of the Dome Extension, below the Dome 23rd level, where drill holes showed more than a score of gold intersections in an area measuring 400 by 700 feet. Bache predicted, "There will certainly be several orebodies."

At this time C.W. Dowsett, the former General Superintendent, returned to Canada from South Africa and was engaged by Dome as a consulting metallurgist. He plunged immediately into an improvement program of gold recovery which increased extraction of gold by 3.29 per cent to 98.3 per cent. On Dowsett's recommendation the Company built a small plant to recover gold from the fine iron waste from the grinding mills and ashes from the 1929 fire, initially recovering 3,400 ounces of gold from this source.

After the death of DePencier in 1935, Joseph H. Stovel, with Dome since 1928 and Assistant General Manager for only two years, was appointed to the top management position, and Robert E. Dye became General Superintendent at South Porcupine.

Dome continued to venture into distant fields, looking for properties it could develop. A group of claims held under option in the Swayze district of Ontario were examined for a year but subsequently dropped when no worthwhile finds were made. Prospecting in South Africa was eventually discontinued because of poor results. As well, under the direction of DePencier, Dome had optioned 21 claims in Bourlamaque Township, which were held under charter by Read-Authier Mines Limited. A promising outcrop had been found on these claims but extensive overburden made it difficult to trace on the surface. Underground work from a small shaft and diamond drilling indicated two potential ore zones which, while interesting, "did not permit of a definite conclusion as to the merits of the property," said DePencier shortly before his death. Several months later, Stovel was pleased to report that the work at the Sigma property, as it was called, was "sufficiently encouraging to warrant the continuation of our development campaign." (The Sigma story is continued in Chapter 10.)

Dome management did not neglect its primary operation, the Big Dome, during these activities. Thirteen claims were acquired from Foley O'Brien Corporation when Dome engineers had projected that the strike of some of their orebodies lay in that direction. However, said Joe Stovel, "it may be several years before our workings reach this property."

The acquisition of another neighbouring property was one of the very few times that Jules Bache, an astute financier, ran second in a business deal. The property, 160 acres in all, had been purchased by Frederick W. Schumacher, a wealthy pharmacist and Vice-President of The Peruna Company of Columbus, Ohio, who had become interested in the mining possibilities of Ontario after the Cobalt rush. He engaged two Ohio state geologists, Shirley Cragg and Morgan Millen, to report on the potential of prospects in the area. Although Millen was not optimistic, Cragg presented a glowing report on the future of Porcupine gold mining. The American decided to risk $8,000 on the purchase of several "Veteran lots," which the Crown had given to veterans of the volunteer militia who served in the Fenian Raids of 1866 and those of the Boer War of 1899 in recognition of their services. One of these lots, adjacent to the mighty Hollinger mine, was incorporated as Schumacher Gold Mines Ltd. in 1914 and produced gold bullion valued at $564,984 until it closed in 1918. In June, 1922, Hollinger purchased the 160-acre property, with its 150-ton mill, for $1,733,333.

In 1911, Schumacher decided to offer, through one Archie Fuller, another 160-acre lot to Dome for $75,000, which was turned down. In *Free Gold*, Arnold Hoffman relates that Schumacher directed Fuller to tell the Dome management that if they changed their minds, the price would double. Dome greeted this, Hoffman writes, "with derision and laughter." However, over the next few years, Dome realized that the Schumacher property was becoming increasingly important and offered $75,000, but were confronted with a demand for $150,000 and the repeated stipulation that this would increase to $300,000 if turned down. Bache would have preferred to drop the whole matter then and there, but by this time underground work was drawing uncomfortably close to the Schumacher claims, thereby running the risk of a claim for huge damages for trespassing. He reluctantly agreed to $150,000, which the wily owner spurned, insisting that the price was now $600,000. Furious, Bache halted all dealings with Schumacher.

Dome executives and engineers made private overtures to the stubborn Schumacher, who was adamant that the price would remain at $600,000 unless turned down, when it would again double. In 1936, twenty-five years after the first offer, Dome reluctantly purchased the land from Schumacher for $1,125,000 and 20,000 shares of Dome stock, worth at the time about $600,000, and twenty-three times the original price of $75,000. Fortunately, the production from the Schumacher claims upheld Bache's belief that "developments . . . are such that we have no hesitation in saying that the purchase will be amply justified." In the first decade of Dome ownership, gold valued at many times the price paid to Schumacher was recovered from only four acres in one corner of the property. As for Fred Schumacher, Hoffman noted, $8,000 gave him a return of nearly $2 million — "not, after all, a bagatelle," although he had to wait 25 years.

Over its long history, Dome had other chances to develop properties, which unfortunately were not taken for a variety of justifiable reasons. One missed opportunity involved Dome's former chief geologist, Douglas Wright, who had joined forces with Jack Hammell in the venture that became the successful Howey mine. Several years later, during the depressed thirties, Wright again tried to interest Dome in a property, another deal which the Company turned down.

The property, 120 acres southeast of Dome's ground, was a prospect known as Preston East Dome. When the disastrous forest fire of 1911 devastated the district, the new mine's plant was also destroyed. For the next two decades, Preston East Dome lay dormant, with little interest taken by anyone in the possibility of its revival. Then, when the price of gold began to rise in the thirties, many properties that had long been idle were considered for reopening. One of the mining men who saw a future for Preston East Dome was Douglas Wright.

Wright's first step was to acquire control of the property through the purchase of stock, as well as picking up additional acreage near the main property. He then turned to Preston East Dome's powerful neighbour and offered the entire package to Dome Mines for $50,000. The response was negative — economic conditions were bad, money was hard to come by, and Dome management was not interested in taking on what might turn out to be a burden rather than an asset. The response was the same when Wright tried to interest other investors in Preston East Dome.

Wright appeared to have another body on his hands for what mining engineer Arnold Hoffman has called "the ample graveyard of mining cadavers," until he heard that a New York entrepreneur named Hirshhorn might be receptive to a proposal.

Hirshhorn was born in Brooklyn, New York, and his life was not unlike that of a rags-to-riches Horatio Alger hero. Leaving school at a young age, he worked as a telegraph messenger and then compiled charts for a financial journal, picking up a great deal of knowledge about stocks and bonds. Before long he was a trader himself on the New York Curb Exchange, attracting the attention of important businessmen who occasionally commissioned him to carry out special assignments, one of which was a study of the Toronto Mining Exchange. The success of that assignment led to other work in Canada. Hirshhorn, convinced that there was a bright future for mining in Canada, opened a brokerage office in Toronto in 1932, at a time when others were closing their doors. His first step was to introduce himself to Canadians by means of a large advertisement in *The Northern Miner*, in which he painted a glowing picture of mining and its benefits for all Canadians.

After hearing Wright's story, Hirshhorn lost no time in agreeing to his proposal. Preston East Dome, drilled so many times in its brief history, was drilled once more, but this time the first two holes indicated prosperity for Wright and Hirshhorn. Production was underway by 1939 and the company's bonds were paid off within one year. Preston East Dome became one of the leaders among Canadian gold mines until the exhaustion of its ore reserves almost thirty years later. Total production to December 31, 1968, was valued at $57,223,000 from 6,293,400 tons of ore. Dividends paid amounted to $28,459,400.

In 1935, the 25th year of Dome's corporate existence, the Company had 790 employees and an annual payroll of $1,438,142. Two years later, Dome introduced its pension plan, to which both the Company and employees contributed, which was at that time a rarity in the industrial world. Ninety per cent of Dome's workers signed up and six took their pensions and retired immediately, as the Company covered all retroactive costs.

Meanwhile, in Europe, Adolf Hitler was uttering such threats that Neville Chamberlain hastened to Munich to try for "peace in our time." Canadians, however, were more concerned with overcoming the depression than with the possibility of war. Dome seemed to recover by 1938, reporting a net operating profit of $4,731,289. Federal, provincial and municipal taxes, though, amounted to $733,501, and that, Bache noted, was in excess of 10 per cent of the gross output of $7,293,288 in bullion. Already, more than a year before Canada found herself at war, tax increases were a serious concern to management and shareholders. Despite this, it had been a good period for Dome and the capital stock was divided two for one.

Continuing exploration taking place some three decades after Dome's discovery was already far removed from the life of the early prospectors graphically described by J.B. MacDougall in *Two Thousand Miles of Gold*:

> . . . For him it is the Great Adventure. The germ of conquest is in his blood. Day by day he drives a wedge deeper into the unknown. He looks to far horizons. By day he tramps and picks, and scans the ground. By night he kindles his campfire under the lone stars. He eats his meagre meal in silence. He grinds the day's samples in his mortar and pans the product by the side of the creek. He scrutinizes the residue for a trace of the yellow dust. Ninety-nine times out of a hundred he fails. But he

goes on, failing yet unbeaten. Night finds him fagged out. He tosses himself on his bed of balsam boughs under the open skies. By dawn he's fresh for the trail again . . .

The increased use of aircraft for exploratory purposes was the first major step toward the end of the "real viking of the trail." Where formerly one or two men had struggled for months to reach a promising site, a small, noisy bush plane could now accomplish the same trip in a few hours or days. Education, rather than years of hard-won practical experience, began to play a significant role in the finding of new mines. Attendance at mining departments of universities was on the upswing, and the teamwork of specialists, based on cold scientific reasoning, soon replaced the romantic (although at times amazingly accurate) "hunches."

These changes resulted in more efficient prospecting, narrowing down the vast unexplored regions to those most likely to contain potential mines. Dome had continued modest prospecting forays in the west, dispatching a crew of four prospectors headed by Walter Cliff to the Yellowknife district of the Northwest Territories. They first staked 43 claims on a discovery they made in the Pensive Lake area, and a diamond drill crew drilled 23 holes, the deepest of which was 468 feet. Although surface showings produced an average value of $8.37 per ton in gold, values from the vein under the outcrop were lower and erratic. Later, in 1938, Dome optioned another group of claims nearby but these failed to yield satisfactory results.

Another crew of twenty men moved into Dome property north of Yellowknife for prospecting and sampling. They soon realized that the showings were too low a grade to be profitable especially in such a remote region. However, it was decided to record the work done and keep the claims valid for several years.

Recognizing the growing importance of exploration, Dome increased spending to $100,213 in 1939. In May of that year, the Company established a wholly-owned subsidiary, Dome Exploration Company (Quebec) Limited, to carry out exploration activities in that province.

Dome managed to come through an economically difficult decade with a record of which it could well be proud. Ahead lay another period of promise in central and western Canada, although the Nazi onslaught upon Poland and the entry of Canada, Britain and France into the conflict created a black cloud on the horizon.

James G.L. McCrea

CHAPTER 10

The Sigma Mine

In Abitibi County, Quebec, the land is marshy, unsuitable for farming or anything else — at least, so people said. No one could have known that one day a prosperous community would spring up in the gently rolling countryside on the shores of Lac Blouin whose very name excites the imagination: Val d'Or, or Valley of Gold.

Although fur traders had dealt with the local Indians, the Abitibbians, who belonged to the Great Algonquin family, and a few explorers and missionaries had reached Lake Abitibi during the French regime, the presence of mineral riches in the inland regions was never suspected. It was not until 1887 that the Geological Survey of Canada sent Dr. Robert Bell and A.S. Cochrane to investigate the vicinity of Lac Blouin. Favourable indications of minerals had been discovered in northwestern Quebec, but the area was so remote, so infested with pesky black flies and mosquitoes in the summer and so costly to develop, that few took the prospect seriously. However, near the lower Ottawa River, iron, mica and graphite mines had already been established and the province had passed its General Mining Act in 1880.

In order to open up this vast but sparsely populated area, and attract young people to the region, the Quebec government established a new colonization policy. To further open up the Abitibi frontier, the businessmen of Quebec City eagerly promoted the construction of the National Transcontinental Railway, later to be absorbed by the Canadian National Railways. In 1912, the railway began bringing thousands of hardy pioneers to the region. It was initially supposed that agriculture and forestry would dominate the local economy, but it proved to be mining that eventually became the most important component.

In light of this slow development, it seems ironic that Canada's first authenticated gold discovery was made in Quebec in 1823, when a surprised farm woman plucked a nugget from the waters of the Gilbert River, a tributary of the Chaudière River. At various times during the ensuing years, placer gold was recovered from other rivers in this region.

The mining rush in northeastern Ontario in the first decade of this century provided two major reasons for the establishment of a mining industry in Quebec. First, it soon became evident that there were two long "breaks" in the earth's crust creating favourable geological conditions for ore deposits in Ontario, and extending some distance into Quebec. Second, the Ontario gold rushes had fostered a class of experienced prospectors and developers willing to risk capital to develop Quebec's untapped resources.

The first real find in the Abitibi area was made in 1907 by two French-Canadians on the shores of a small lake named Lac Fortune. The resulting mine, although unsuccessful, interested several Ontario prospectors, including John Beattie, Joe Sullivan and Stanley Siscoe, who all made finds. The dawn of the First World War slowed the pace somewhat, but Ed Horne was still able to carry out his famous explorations which led to the founding of the Noranda Mine, followed closely by Tom Powell's discovery of gold at Rouyn in 1922.

One person who was well aware of these developments and who would soon play an important role in the making of Dome's Sigma Mines was Hector Authier, a former journalist and lawyer, who arrived in Amos, a bustling town on the newly-opened National Transcontinental Railway, in 1912. He was appointed by the Quebec government to act as agent for lands and mines for the Abitibi district, and soon became Amos' first mayor.

By the late twenties, nearby Bourlamaque Township, named after an aide-de-camp to the French hero Montcalm, had become a seat of vigorous exploratory activity and Authier formed a company to assemble land for mining development. Read-Authier Mines Limited was formed under a Quebec charter on October 28, 1928, with an authorized capital of three million shares of $1 par value. Serving the company were Hector Authier as President, William A. Read of London, England, as Vice-President, and Louis Brochu of Montreal as Secretary.

According to Raoul Blanchard, an historian of the Abitibi district, the Read-Authier Company was gathering claims in Bourlamaque as early as 1931. A test pit had been sunk in 1929 on a vein in the southwest corner of the group by the previous owners and some samples containing free gold were obtained, but the owners lacked both the money and the experience necessary to further develop the claims. In late 1932, Teck Hughes Gold Mines of Kirkland Lake, Ontario, became actively involved in the south group of claims, and formed the very profitable Lamaque Gold Mines, in which Read-Authier retained a 30 per cent interest.

Gold prices began to rise slowly in 1933, but it was not until the following February that U.S. President Franklin D. Roosevelt devalued the U.S. dollar, and the official price of gold jumped from $20.67 to $35 an ounce. This acted as

Jim Redpath at door of first log cabin on Read-Authier property which later became Sigma Mines in 1934. (left)

Jim McCrea and Jim Redpath welcome distinguished visitors to Sigma Mines. Left to right: Eugene Larochelle, Dick Pearce, Jim McCrea, Quebec Mines Minister Jonathan Robinson, George Smelzer, Deputy Minister Alphonse Dufresne, Jim Redpath. (below)

a great stimulus to the Canadian gold mining industry, particularly in Ontario and Quebec.

In 1933, Read-Authier sent a consulting engineer, Heber Bambrick, to join a crew prospecting on their remaining claims. These claims were accessible in the summer by a rough three-mile wagon road from Lac Blouin, at the end of a 58-mile water route from Amos, and in winter by sleigh from the Canadian National Railways station 38 miles north at Barraute, situated 25 miles east of Amos. Bambrick discovered a vein which produced some encouraging results after trenching 300 feet along its strike, followed by sampling and diamond drilling. Dome was invited to take a look, and James G. McCrea, Chief Exploration Engineer, was so impressed by the Bourlamaque find that his enthusiastic recommendation to purchase was immediately accepted by H.P. DePencier. By the end of January, 1934, James B. Redpath, a recent graduate in mining engineering from McGill University, who had been hired by Dome as an exploration engineer, also sampled the showings and checked the work being done, with favourable results. An agreement to purchase, dated February 20, 1934, was made with Read-Authier, and Sigma Mines Limited was subsequently formed under federal charter on April 21, 1934, with an authorized capital of 3,000,000 shares. Read-Authier retained 40 per cent, and the remaining 60 per cent was optioned to Dome under an agreement that $600,000 would be spent on development.

Directors of the new Company were James Aitchison, C.C. Calvin and J.B. Robinson, lawyers in the Fasken law firm, Hector Authier and Louis Brochu. Officers were James Aitchison as President and C.C. Calvin as Secretary. Alexander Fasken later replaced Aitchison as President. Additional managerial appointments were Joseph H. Stovel as General Manager, James G. McCrea as Assistant General Manager, and James B. Redpath as Superintendent. McCrea, who was responsible for operating the property in the crucial start-up years, later became General Manager and then Vice-President, with Redpath succeeding him in both positions.

The renowned Sigma mine is located at the eastern boundary of Val d'Or, about 60 miles from the Ontario border, in the Abitibi district.

The ink was scarcely dry on the agreement when 90 tons of equipment and supplies were transported to the site and a mining plant erected which included accommodations for fifty men. Before the year-end, almost 11,000 feet of drilling had been carried out, revealing a main ore zone 1,200 feet in length and 250 feet deep. Another zone yielding spectacular high-grade specimens was discovered running parallel 200 feet northwards. A shaft was sunk on the south zone to a depth of 264 feet on an incline of 65 degrees, following the dip of the main vein. Work proceeded rapidly despite a series of mechanical failures and the heavy inflow of spring thaw and swamp waters which entered the underground workings through the many exploratory drill holes. During the first year of operations, 5,356 feet of underground development partially opened up the two zones, revealing ore of excellent grade and widths, and *The Northern Miner* reported to its readers: "An efficient piece of neat mining has been carried out."

General Manager Jim McCrea disclosed that the average value of ore removed during shaft-sinking was $19.56 per ton (with gold at $35 per ounce). This very good grade could not, however, be expected to extend over the whole property, although McCrea had observed free gold in every round blasted, to a depth of 45 feet, and again at 90 feet. The original inclined shaft, while good for exploratory purposes, was unsuitable for mining operations. As a result, in June, 1935, a vertical shaft was sunk to a depth of 1,000 feet, and equipped with a steel headframe and an electric hoist capable of lifting 500 tons per day from a depth of 2,000 feet.

Rumours began circulating that a mill would soon be erected at Sigma, but management insisted that any such decision would have to await confirmation of orebodies on the bottom levels. A composite picture of the underground structure was gradually assembled and, although the ore was irregularly distributed in seven zones, an intelligent plan of exploration quickly brought the mine to a point where 62 per cent of all development was within the ore which, commented *The Northern Miner*, "is a very good percentage for this type of mine."

Late in June, 1936, diamond drilling confirmed the continuity of ore down to 1,000 feet, and the Sigma mill was given the green light. C.W. Dowsett was again engaged by Dome, along with his partner, William Dunn, to recommend the process that would be most suitable for the treatment of ore and to design the mill. The conventional straight cyanide treatment was decided upon, with the mill capable of handling 300 tons a day and increasing to 500 tons when required, which proved to be only a year later.

One of the few chemicals that can dissolve gold is sodium or potassium cyanide, a highly toxic chemical which dissolves easily in water. When in solution, it slowly attacks fine particles of gold, releasing them (and any associated silver particles) from the surrounding rock and ultimately dissolving them. Lime is added to the solution, because it protects the cyanide from being destroyed by some naturally occurring minerals called cyanicides, and also because it accelerates the settlement of the gold precipitate. Since oxygen is needed for the reaction to occur, a weak solution (with a high proportion of water) attacks the gold particles faster than a strong solution. In certain ores, the addition of air speeds up the slow (ten to fifty hours) dissolution process to some degree.

After the gold has been dissolved, fine zinc dust is added to the solution, which causes the gold to precipitate to the bottom in a sludge-like mass. This sludge takes on its muddy appearance due to the black zinc dust and impurities, such as sulphides, from the original ore. The gold-cyanide precipitate is mixed with fluxes, refined in an oil-fired furnace and finally poured into molds, forming gold bullion bars which may be 90-98 per cent pure gold and silver. Coarse gold particles in the original ore are usually removed by gravity separation and may be added to the melt in the refining process. Gold bullion bars are then shipped to the Royal Canadian Mint in Ottawa for further refining and separation of the silver.

The mill announcement excited the boom town that had sprung up nearby. Val d'Or began in 1933 with a few shacks lining a muddy street in the middle of nowhere, but shortly after the Sigma mill commenced production on St. Patrick's Day, 1937, it had received its charter as a town, sported dance halls and gambling houses, and boasted a population of 7,000.

Sigma had developed sufficient reserves to supply the mill for two years, and before the end of 1937 had treated 125,407 tons of ore, extracting gold to the value of $991,551. "This has been a splendid start," beamed Joe Stovel. A year later, the Sigma mill at 650 tons per day was actually exceeding the designed capacity by 30 per cent. The milling rate rose steadily each month, reflecting the spectacular productivity of the mine. In late 1939, 750 tons a day were being processed, and by 1940, new equipment brought the rate to 1,000 tons daily. Two years later the mill was again running a hundred tons above capacity. Fortunately, the building had originally been designed with extra room to accommodate this expansion.

In 1937, as a result of the passing of Bill 5 of the Quebec legislature, it became necessary for Sigma to be newly chartered under the name of Sigma Mines (Quebec) Limited. The old Sigma, capitalized at 3,000,000 shares, had been split between Dome and Read-Authier; the new Company was capitalized at 1,000,000 shares, the holders receiving one share of the new for each three of the old.

During a lengthy lull in mining news, one persistent reporter for a Toronto financial newspaper visited the Sigma mine over a period of two years without getting any "news" of consequence from the friendly but reserved McCrea. Perhaps wanting to save the frustrated reporter unnecessary trips, the General Manager finally remarked, "You know, we mine and mill nearly half a million tons of ore each year, which must be replaced with new ore just to maintain reserves. If we are just holding even, we are making no news . . . It's a good mine that makes no news — and we make no news."

The role played by Read-Authier in Sigma's history was soon to end. A policy of the syndicate had been that it would hold its stock assets intact until its prize offspring, Lamaque and Sigma, became dividend-payers. Accordingly, as this would obviously occur in the very near future, Read-Authier surrendered its charter late in 1938. For each hundred shares of Read-Authier held, a stockholder received 38 shares of Lamaque Mines, 21 shares of Sigma, and 100 shares of Union Mining Corporation, holder of some old Read-Authier claims adjacent to the Lamaque and Sigma properties. On January 16, 1939, Sigma was listed on the Toronto Stock Exchange and opened at $5.50 per share, reaching a high of $6.40 on its first day.

The late thirties and early forties were exciting years for Sigma, with records broken each year either for tonnage or production value. The Company soon acquired new lots to build housing for many of its 350 employees and adopted Dome's policy of giving its workers 50 per cent pay for up to six months in times of illness, an extremely generous arrangement for the time.

Sigma was still a promising young company with considerable property to explore. A programme of extensive underground drilling was pursued, probing both downwards and horizontally. The pattern of the orebodies within the geological structure was becoming clear and, gradually, a routine of exploration and development evolved which best suited its peculiarities. In 1938, it was decided that the main shaft would be sunk to 2,000 feet. By the end of the next year, Sigma had 16 underground levels, although few past the fourth could be mined until the delivery of a larger hoist, which would be able to raise greater tonnage from an eventual depth of 3,000 feet.

By the fall of 1939, advances made to Sigma by Dome and Read-Authier were repaid and shareholders were looking forward to dividends. In 1941, Sigma paid $600,000 to shareholders, of which $360,000 went to Dome, greatly assisting the latter to meet its commitments to its own shareholders.

The year 1942 was a record one, with 403,467 tons of ore milled and production valued at $3,055,372. Diamond drilling revealed ore intersections 400 feet below the bottom level but detailed exploration had to be postponed. After three years of war, the mining industry now plunged into a period of declining production and reduced revenue. A rise in the value of the Canadian dollar, *vis-à-vis* the U.S. dollar, resulted in a reduction in the price of gold, since it was fixed at $35 (U.S.) an ounce. Because of this, the Company was forced to cut dividends during the war. Labour shortages were also beginning to affect operations. In 1942, there were 10,000 mine workers in Abitibi County. Of these, 25 per cent had left by 1945. In addition, Sigma staff members were being called upon to help develop Dome's Indian Molybdenum property, molybdenum being a crucial wartime material. A substantial reduction in diamond drilling resulted and mill production was cut to around 800 tons a day for the duration of the war. To maintain this reduced level, it was necessary to work the most accessible areas of the mine, even if this meant lower grades. The high-grade "flats," which generally required more labour for each ton extracted, would have to wait until the manpower situation improved.

Though Sigma's situation appeared gloomy, at least temporarily, Joe Stovel gave this encouraging view in his final annual report for Dome in 1944:

> As I write this report, it is actually slightly less than 10 years since Dome took its original option on the property that is now known as Sigma Mines. Sigma has settled down so quickly into a steadily producing mine and one with a most promising future that even those of us most actively concerned with it are apt to forget that only 10 years ago the site, where now stands this splendid plant, was wholly covered with the original forest. The original surface showing, which resulted in the option being taken, still is undisturbed and every time I see it I marvel that this showing led to a real mine . . .
>
> Anyone who has recently seen Sigma Mines and its surroundings can readily realize what an asset a new gold mine is to its own locality and to the country in general. In money spent on wages, equipment, supplies, power, etc., and in gold produced, it has proved an important factor in our national economic life and I venture that it will continue to hold that role for many years to come . . .

Even when the war was over, the labour situation continued to deteriorate. As McCrea had forecast at Sigma's Annual Meeting in 1945, new industries created during the war were able to stay in business, and a number of new mines whose openings had been delayed were now underway. Despite these pressures, Sigma was one of the first mining companies to return to normal production levels after the war. By 1948, sufficient manpower had become available, mainly because of the influx of European workers who immigrated after signing contracts with the Company. Most of the industrious and consistent workers continued working at the mine even after their contracts had expired, in order to bring their families to this prosperous country.

As Sigma entered the fifties, it already had an admirable record to look back on. Since 1937, over three million tons of ore had passed through its mill, and ore reserves had more than quadrupled. Despite these achievements, the fifties were characterized by rising costs and fluctuating gold prices due to erratic exchange rates. These pressures were moderated by the Emergency Gold Mining Assistance (EGMA) Act, proclaimed in 1948, which provided assistance by making up some of the difference between the fixed gold price of $35 (U.S.) per ounce and the actual cost of production, and thereby slowing down mine closings. (A more detailed explanation of EGMA is given in Chapter 13.)

Sigma began deepening its main shaft to 3,000 feet, giving the mine 24 underground levels. James Redpath, who succeeded McCrea as General Manager in 1951, pointed out that this deepening would prepare for the future and did not interfere with day-to-day mining operations. The main shaft was located roughly in the centre of the ore zones and, when a new level was opened, cross-cuts were extended north and south across the mineralized area, intersecting the dozen or so prominent vertical veins. The strongest vein was then selected and drifting would commence in an east-west direction, with headings cut periodically to the other veins in preparation for later development. The upper levels were, of course, still very active but were usually mined out first to prevent bottlenecks in hoisting. Even after these levels had officially reached the "clean-up" stage, lucrative flat veins kept turning up. Because of this, it was not until 1956 that the first level was finally exhausted, and the second level lasted until 1962. Sigma later filled the abandoned areas with classified mill tailings to ensure the stability of other underground workings.

In September, 1953, Jim McCrea, Vice-President for two years, died after a brief illness. Redpath moved to Toronto in December as Executive Vice-President of Dome Mines and Vice-President of Sigma, and Frank O'Connell, Assistant General Manager since 1952, succeeded Redpath as General Manager of Sigma.

One summer in the early fifties, when Sigma was barely scraping by with the assistance of the EGMA Act, a mining engineer visited the property. Passing through the gate, he asked O'Connell about a large pile of crushed ore he had noticed underneath the inclined belt conveyor leading from the crushing plant to the ore bins in the mill building, caused, he guessed, by some trouble with the conveyor system. O'Connell, laughing, reassured him. The Company had recently made a contract with the local authorities to supply crushed rock for the construction of paved roads in the region. A by-pass had been installed partway up the conveyor and waste rock from underground was being handled by the plant when it was not crushing ore. This "ore" that the visitor had seen was being spilled-off on its way up the conveyor system to make a pile from which trucks could be loaded. The ironic part of the story was that the Company was making more profit per ton from the sale of the crushed waste rock than it was making per ton of ore treated!

In 1958, Sigma decided to sink a new underground shaft from the 24th level, which would take the mine down to at least the 30th level. This project, which would take two years to complete and cost about $1.2 million, and which was to be financed entirely from earnings, caused a subsequent reduction in dividends.

The sixties started with record tonnages, when drifting on the new bottom levels indicated ore shoots of a grade comparable with that in the upper part of the mine. However, earnings fluctuated throughout the decade as the industry endured the pressure of rising costs, principally wages. Despite labour unrest elsewhere, the Sigma workers, who had formed their own independent union in 1954, remained on good terms with management as they realistically tied their expectations to those of the industry. The 1961 contract, for instance, contained provisions that negotiations would be reopened if other mines in the district increased wages during the three-year term, or if the price of gold rose significantly.

In recognition of its outstanding safety record, Sigma was awarded the annual John T. Ryan Trophy For Mine Safety for "Quebec and East" on six occasions — 1948, 1950, 1960, 1975, 1977 and 1981. In 1950, and again in 1960, the mine won the All-Canada Trophy, presented to the metal mine in Canada having the lowest accident frequency. To celebrate the Company's success in providing the safest possible working environment for its employees, a dance for 800 people was held in 1960. This gala event was attended by Sigma employees, their families, and federal and provincial government officials.

In 1966, Frank O'Connell died suddenly, a great loss to the mining industry. His contributions in the areas of mining methods and safety were outstanding and, in his memory, a trophy for the best safety record is presented annually by the Quebec Mines Accident Prevention Association. O'Connell's replacement as General Manager was George E. Peacock, General Superintendent and Assistant General Manager since 1954. When first introduced by the Chairman to the shareholders at Campbell's annual meeting, Peacock, a portly bald man, drew himself up to his full six-foot-plus height and stoutly announced: "My name is Peacock and I've come without my feathers!" At this time Gordon Michaelson, employed at Dome, Indian Molybdenum, Mindamar and Sigma for over thirty years, was named General Superintendent. In 1970, Peacock was transferred to Campbell Red Lake, and Malcolm Taschereau was named General Manager.

The end of the sixties witnessed new records for tonnage and production. Nevertheless, the fixed price of gold was becoming an increased burden in the face of inflation, and the EGMA Act became inadequate. In 1969, Redpath announced that even with unprecedented gold production, Sigma profits were low because of the severe cost-price squeeze. It was whispered that the mine had only a few more years of life left and that by 1975 it would become one of the many abandoned sites in Abitibi County. But, once again, the rumours proved unfounded. The Company undertook a programme of cost reduction by introducing a number of newer, more efficient methods. For example, one small saving was achieved when new atomic absorption equipment for ore analysis was introduced into the assay office, where more than 6,000 samples were processed each month. This technique saved an estimated $10,000 yearly over the previous fire assay method.

The profit picture changed dramatically in August, 1971, when U.S. President Richard Nixon ended the gold exchange standard and ushered in the current monetary system, liberating gold to find its own market price. The results were spectacular. In 1972, Sigma began selling its gold on the free market, disqualifying it for EGMA benefits, but resulting in a significant increase in revenue. The following year saw another major price hike for gold and Sigma's net profits doubled. Moreover, the high return encouraged the extraction and treatment of formerly uneconomical low-grade ore, further extending the life of the mine.

Between August, 1972, and May, 1974, shaft No. 3, the internal shaft, was sunk to 5,780 feet, where a 40th level was established. Improvements in the mill raised its capacity to 1,460 tons daily, and General Manager Taschereau felt that the mine had "a substantial number of years ahead of it and, hopefully, good profitable ones at that."

Although costs and taxes continued to rise, Sigma enjoyed substantial earnings in the late seventies. In 1943, Jules Bache, President of Dome Mines, had spoken about the "instinctive desire for gold" that would assert itself "among all people weary of inflated paper money." This prediction now proved most accurate, as people scrambled to possess the precious yellow metal. Under the pressure of severe demand and general worry over international situations, the Canadian price soared from $161 in 1977 to $610 at the end of 1979. Some observers even foresaw an eventual $1,000 an ounce. For Sigma, 89,081 ounces in 1970 had produced revenues of $3.3 million. By contrast, however, in 1979, although it produced 24 per cent *less* gold, the Company earned $24.5 million and its stock hit a high of $42.50 a share on the Toronto Stock Exchange.

Extensive exploration continued on the Sigma property as the eighties began. The overall philosophy now was to emphasize prolongation of mine life which would entail treatment of lower grade ore and perhaps reduced production. "The mine has been going for forty-two years," said the Assistant Manager, André Carrier, in 1979, "and we'd like it to go for another forty-two." Sigma also branched out beyond its boundaries, exploring land in Louvicourt Township, 20 miles east of Val d'Or, and participating with Dome in various ventures outside Ontario and Quebec, while undertaking all of the Dome group's exploration activities in the latter province.

Sigma Mines plant, with town of Val d'Or in background.

In 1977, Malcolm A. Taschereau became President, and a year later assumed the additional post of Chairman. Bernard H. Joyal, Mine Manager since 1975, became General Manager in 1980, and André Carrier was appointed Assistant General Manager in 1981. Sigma had no difficulty meeting the requirements of Quebec's recent linguistic regulations since its staff and work force were always primarily francophone. In 1979, the Company launched an annual programme of stock distribution among employees based on years of service and also significantly improved the pension plan. Sigma is well integrated into the Val d'Or community and its economic importance can be judged by a 1979 study which found that over 80 per cent of Sigma's supplies came from within Quebec, with about half of that purchased from local vendors. By the end of the decade the mine employed nearly 400 persons.

By the end of 1981, Sigma had produced over $260 million worth of gold since its start in 1937. This achievement is even more remarkable when one remembers how disparagingly this area was once thought of and how nobody was interested in the wasteland that truly became a "valley of gold."

CHAPTER 11

The Second World War and the Dome

The conflict into which the world was plunged in September, 1939, had an immediate effect on Canadian mining companies. Dome Mines Limited was not immune and three major problems soon emerged: the shortage of manpower, the government's attitude toward the mining industry, and the growing tax burden.

Within two years, more than 200 of Dome's work force were serving in the armed forces, with the Company's assurances that their jobs and their pension and insurance rights would be protected. In addition to these predictable labour losses, the Department of Munitions and Supply in Ottawa was empowered by an Order-in-Council to mobilize manpower for the production of war supplies, and decided to transfer another fifty of Dome's employees to jobs in the Sudbury nickel mines, which were regarded as more essential to the war effort. "For a time," commented Joe Stovel, "labour conditions were almost chaotic." The shortage of certain supplies was also increasingly difficult to cope with. "Necessity has driven us to improvise and to substitute in many ways not thought possible previously," he said.

These strained conditions were being closely watched by observers of the Canadian mining scene. Many had doubts about the quality of the ore on the Dome property and were pessimistic about its future, a view shared by some of the more conservative members of Dome management. But a more reassuring opinion was held by at least one staunch Dome supporter. In the summer of 1940, a reader wrote to *The Northern Miner* and asked: "I have 100 shares of Dome up as collateral on a loan at the bank. Do you think Dome's present position and future possibilities warrant holding this stock for the duration of the war?" The editor saw nothing wrong with the future of Dome, even in those difficult times: "We cannot see any reason why Dome should not continue to earn and pay its dividend during the years ahead . . . The mine is in excellent shape, perhaps the best ever."

Dome's staff took an active part in the war effort overseas and made significant contributions on the home front. Joe Stovel represented the mining industry on the National War Labour Board, which attempted to maintain industrial stability, while at the same time encouraging equitable returns for workers through the administration of wage controls and improved working conditions. Robert Dye and other senior staff members served on local committees such as the Red Cross, War Bond Drives, Volunteer Reserve Training, the Emergency Measures Organization, St. John's Ambulance, the Victorian Order of Nurses, and a War Charities Fund.

Working closely with the pulp and paper industry, Dome acted as a subcontractor and co-ordinator of a major project to manufacture parts and equipment for steam-operated reciprocating pumps for the "Fort" and "Park" series of cargo vessels being built in Canadian shipyards on both east and west coasts. These were the Canadian equivalent of the U.S. "Liberty" ships, which were built rapidly to replace Allied losses by German submarines. Rough foundry castings and other materials were shipped to Dome, which distributed them to those mines in the district supporting the project. When necessary, the well-equipped shops operated round-the-clock on "war work," machining parts to exact specifications. At Dome the pumps were assembled, tested in the presence of a Lloyd's of London inspector, and then crated and shipped to their destinations. Under agreement with the federal government, all work at the mines was done at cost. The volume of work was roughly equivalent to $1 million annually and was the direct responsibility of Charles G. Kemsley, Mechanical Superintendent. Letters of commendation presented to Dome by the Canadian government attested to the high quality of work.

In May, 1942, Stovel, now a Vice-President as well as General Manager, stated his view of world conditions:

> After the war I believe that our gold mines will again take the very important place in our national life that they took in the days of our depression. It is, however, the immediate future which concerns us now . . . We have reason to believe that the Canadian government still desires all possible gold production. The pressure of recent events, however, would seem to make that desire second to war requirements (a reference to official pressure on Dome to develop a molybdenum ore property) and where manpower and supplies are needed for our war efforts, one may safely assume that the government will not be able to supply all our requirements . . . We continue to lose men to the armed forces and to war industry . . . These conditions will grow progressively worse . . .

Early in 1937 the Company started to accumulate a supply of

such material as we thought would be the hardest to get if a war came. But now there are certain lines of supplies that are no longer available to us at all . . .

To me these conditions point to the need for curtailment of operations so as to conserve essential supplies and thus keep in operation continuously or as long as possible . . . I proposed, as a first step, cutting our daily tonnage from slightly over 1,700 tons to 1,500 tons, and this has already been done. Instead of laying off men, we have allowed the present abnormal labour turnover to bring our labour force down to the required level. As time goes on, further curtailment may be necessary, but I sincerely hope that by these steps we may avoid a total shut-down. Each such step will result in decreased earnings.

Stovel's plans appeared to have succeeded because a year later he told the shareholders that, although 1942 had been a difficult year, "we did succeed in maintaining our daily tonnage at a steady figure and we did not have to drop our dividend rate . . . We were fortunate in that our old-time shrinkage method of stoping left available ore reserves, and that was the sole reason that we were able to keep up our tonnage rate."

Stovel presented an optimistic outlook on the future of Canada's gold mining industry:

The story of Dome Mines can be multiplied many times over when you take the gold industry as a whole. In the pre-war depression days the industry was a tower of strength to the country. In the early years of the war the industry was asked to produce to the limit to help the government maintain its trade balance with the United States.

Graham Towers, Governor of the Bank of Canada, is credited by the press as saying in Toronto that "the gold Canada had at the beginning of the war, and what it still had, saved our bacon." He went on to say: "It is all very well for some people to decry the value of gold, but when you get into a fix, the only thing you can be sure of is the purchasing power of gold, which millions of people all over the world still demand in preference to paper money."

The fundamental position of gold in world economics is unshaken and I believe that many more gold mines will be brought into production if the right conditions prevail. But such conditions do not prevail now. The present burden of taxation should be revised sharply downwards at the end of the

DOME MINES LIMITED 1919

DOME MINES LIMITED 1939

The top photograph made in 1913 and the second made in 1919 show the changing scene at Dome. The third photo shows the extent of the property in 1939.

war and the restrictive regulations which hamper and discourage prospecting should also be revised. The public should have all possible protection against fraudulent promotions but it should also have the opportunity to support legitimate mine development which should carry a reward commensurate with the risk involved. It must be remembered that for every successful mine there are many unsuccessful ones, so that putting money into these ventures is a highly speculative move. In the last analysis it is the public who have the say as to what shall be done and the shareholders in mines are part of that public. They are urged to use their influence and knowledge.

During this time, Dome's prospectors were engaged chiefly in the search for minerals useful to the war effort, one of which was molybdenum, a brittle, silvery-white, flaky mineral used in the making of steel alloys. The finding of what James McCrea described as a "substantial tonnage" of molybdenum ore on Indian Peninsula in Preissac Township in northwestern Quebec led to the inception of Indian Molybdenum Limited in 1943. On McCrea's recommendation, Dome organized the subsidiary to take over the 5,600-acre property which contained a promising orebody that measured 450 feet by 35 feet. Due to the sinking by German submarines of Allied ships carrying this crucial wartime material, the federal government began to pressure domestic sources to produce molybdenum. The government readily agreed to a contract with Dome whereby it would purchase over a two-year period, two million pounds of molybdenum concentrates at 85 cents a pound, nearly double the peacetime price. The government also agreed to pay up to an additional 15 cents a pound to ensure Dome a fair profit on its deliveries. Desperate for "moly," Ottawa pressed Dome to move quickly into plans for a complete mining operation, including a mill with a capacity of 400-500 tons a day. Under this insistent prodding, Dome built the plant, at a cost of $600,000. The contract came at an inopportune time, however, due to persistent labour shortages. By June, 1943, Dome's own mine was down to only 43 per cent of its normal development activity and all work had stopped in the No. 6 shaft below the 16th level. For the most part, work was carried out on the upper levels in a rather compact part of the original Dome claims. Production was as low as 1,450 tons a day. There was only one way Stovel could explain it: "We simply don't have the men."

The same applied to the molybdenum mine. The few workers who had been found came from the small and scattered local farm population, and during the summer of 1943, it was impossible to mine more than 150 tons a day, far below the intended production rate. There was, however, a bright side. The first cross-cut through the molybdenum deposit revealed good widths and grades of ore. Moreover, after the mill went into operation in September, 1943, a scant thirteen months after the discovery of the orebody, production gradually increased to 300 tons a day by the end of the year and later as high as 750 tons. The first shipment of concentrates showed that there were few impurities and the product was of good grade.

Then the unforeseen happened: the market for molybdenum disappeared as suddenly as it had arisen. By the beginning of 1944, the demand for strategic metals needed for munitions dropped sharply. Dome was notified by Ottawa that its contracts were cancelled and on April 30, 1944, Indian Molybdenum ceased operations.

Despite the substantial losses incurred, the act of cancellation of the contract by the government was justified, but Dome felt that it still deserved the supplementary 15 cents a pound originally stipulated in the contract. As a result, Indian Molybdenum took action in the Exchequer Court, claiming a final payment of $104,858, but the action was lost and an appeal to the Supreme Court of Canada was dismissed. Nothing more could be done, except to regard the episode as part of Dome's contribution to the war effort.

There was little possibility of selling "moly" on the open market, as by this time there was enough of the mineral in stock to meet the needs of North American munitions plants for two or three years at the reduced rate of arms production. All was not entirely lost, however, since the mill and plant equipment were later sold to Campbell Red Lake, Dome's newest acquisition and subsidiary.

The years 1943 and 1944 saw some important changes in the management of Dome Mines. After a quarter century of service to the Company, Jules S. Bache resigned from the presidency, due to failing health, and was elected the first Chairman of the Board in August, 1943. This newly-created position in the Dome corporate structure enabled Bache to keep in close contact with operations without having to bear the increasingly heavy work load required of the President.

When the shareholders met in the spring of 1944, Stovel commended Bache's work and recalled an incident related by DePencier. Soon after he became President, Bache summoned DePencier to New York. "The interview was short. Mr. Bache asked what was wrong with the mine and what needed to be done. Mr. DePencier replied that it needed development work – much more development work. Mr. Bache's reply was to go back and get it done. And that was his attitude throughout the term of his presidency. Once the management had presented a reasonable outline of what needed to be done, his invariable answer was to go and get it done. It is no wonder that Mr. DePencier in his day, and I in mine, have had real reason to appreciate and be thankful for the support that Mr. Bache invariably gave us."

The shareholders chose Clifford W. Michel to succeed Bache as President, and elected Stovel as a Director, replacing John G. Baragwanath, a consulting mining engineer from New York who represented the Bernard Baruch interests, and who had resigned due to the pressure of wartime duties.

There were clear signs in North Africa and in Europe that Nazi Germany would soon be overwhelmed by the Allied forces. But for Dome, 1944 was not a happy year. Jules Bache died in March at the age of 83 and the Company suddenly lost the services of Alexander Fasken, its only Secretary since incorporation, when he was killed in an automobile accident near his home in Toronto. The position of Chairman was left vacant and C.C. Calvin, of the Fasken firm and Assistant Secretary since 1923, was appointed Secretary and a Director while F. Hedley Marsh, President of the Bank of Toronto, replaced Bache as a Director.

In addition to these changes, Dome management reluctantly accepted the resignation of Joe Stovel. After more than 40 years in mining, Stovel asked to be relieved of "the burden of supervising daily operations." Clifford Michel told the shareholders that "his services to the Company since 1928 have been of such great value that your Directors only recently would accept his resignation and then with profound regret, and with the proviso that he continue as a member of the Board, and accept the post of Managing Director." A few months later, Robert E. Dye, Assistant General Manager for nine years, was appointed General Manager.

Born in South Dakota, Robert Emmett Dye and his family moved to Joplin, Missouri, where he obtained his Engineer of Mines degree at the Missouri School of Mines in 1915. He headed for Canada and was employed in Cobalt, South Lorraine and Kirkland Lake variously as Mill Superintendent and Mill Manager, and as a teacher at the Haileybury School of Mines until 1922, when he was appointed Manager of the Vipond Mine in Porcupine. Deciding to make Canada his home, he became a citizen in 1932 and moved to Dome as General Superintendent four years later.

On March 1, 1945, Dome, placing great importance upon increased exploration, decided that this could best be managed through a separate corporate entity. Accordingly, a wholly-owned subsidiary named Dome Exploration (Canada) Limited was incorporated with James G. McCrea as General Manager. "We hope," said President Michel, "to intensify our already active search for new properties and companies and be in a position to participate in the expansion which we believe will take place in Canadian mining at the conclusion of the war." One of Dome Exploration's first steps was the taking of an option on shares of Campbell Red Lake Mines Limited late in 1944. Two years later it exercised its option and acquired a 57 per cent interest (the Campbell story is covered in Chapter 14.)

Since new management directed Dome Mines Limited as the Second World War drew to a close, a review of the accomplishments of Jules S. Bache, Alexander Fasken and Joe Stovel is appropriate.

Jules S. Bache
President, 1919-1942
Chairman of the Board, 1943

CHAPTER 12

In Retrospect

"I wonder if the world realizes what it owes, coming out of the depression, to gold mining. It is the only business that has lasted since the first days of investment history; the only investment likely to last is a gold mine. In Dome you have one."

With these words, voiced in 1936, Jules S. Bache expressed his belief in gold and his pride in Dome Mines. Over a quarter of a century with Dome, he never lost faith in his favourite investment and gave the Company strong direction in the aftermath of the First World War, throughout a period of worldwide depression and most of the Second World War.

Bache was assisted by a handpicked team of executives who possessed the knowledge of mining and engineering that he lacked. He also had the counsel of Alexander Fasken, Secretary of Dome Mines, whose Toronto law firm specialized in mining legislation and regulations.

The business acumen displayed by Bache and his associates earned Dome shareholders $56 million in dividends by the end of 1943. In 1918, when Bache first became a Director, gold was selling at $20.67 an ounce and Dome's production was worth $1,480,000. In the twenty-third year of his presidency, production was valued at $7,768,000, with the price of gold fixed at $35.00 (U.S.) an ounce.

His financial management of Dome was not always appreciated. Some Canadian shareholders, on one occasion, complained about the substantial surplus he had built up. Bache defended his actions by replying that an amount had been established as a surplus for Dome and, when attained, future profits would be paid to the shareholders as dividends. This foresight had proved valuable in 1929 when, even though production ceased for a year because of the fire, dividends continued to be paid. However, to placate the disgruntled shareholders, a bonus dividend was paid for 1931, with the promise of future dividends being as generous as the treasury and general conditions at the mine would allow.

After Bache's death in 1944, Wellington Jeffers of the Toronto *Globe and Mail* recalled that he "busied himself mainly at the financial end of the business, but he never missed a shareholders' meeting which he could possibly attend, and there were periods when his robust confidence, determination and sagacity were important factors in retaining the confidence of investors, as showing he was not deterred from his interest when really competent advisers told him not to waste his money in Dome. At times he had more faith in the future of Dome than even the management." Jeffers remembered visiting Dome in January, 1928:

> At that time the great mine was rapidly approaching the end of its marvellous wealth in the sediments, and investment opinion was all agog and uncertain as to whether or not the same good fortune would attend mining in the greenstones. Mr. DePencier told us that their exploration had shown two years' ore ahead of the mine in the greenstones. He was very conservative and would not go a moment of time beyond the two years actually in sight. We wanted to get his opinion on a reading we had secured on the probable prospects beneath the sediments on the basis of work and the trend of orebodies. He was adamant and probably was bending backwards in his idea of what a technical man should say.
>
> A week or so later Mr. Bache made a statement from New York City that the mine would be going strong 10 years from that day. That was his considered judgment, and now, 16 years later, the mine is still going strong and is paying an annual rate of $1.60 a share in dividends in spite of the reduced rate of operations made obligatory by war conditions.

"He was a great optimist," said Alex Fasken, "but he was also keen in a business deal . . . (and) a good man to work with."

Bache loved nothing better than his trips to South Porcupine, where he could meet and talk with the men who actually extracted gold. "He seemed to have a personal affection for the Company, the mine, and all connected with it," Jeffers said. Bache especially enjoyed talking with the older hands about the mine's early days.

Bache was remembered as a friendly and generous man. One Christmas during the Second World War, he asked for a list of the employees serving in the armed forces overseas and sent each $25 as a gift.

His greatest love, other than that he held for Dome, was for fine art. This was possibly inherited from his grandfather, an officer in Napoleon's army who collected art treasures for the Louvre. During his lifetime, Bache amassed a sizable collection of masterpieces, which included tapestries, paintings, sculptures and furniture of the fifteenth to the eighteenth centuries. Some of the paintings were the works of old masters such as Titian, Van Dyck, Durer, Rembrandt and Gainsborough. The entire collection, valued at $12.5 million, was bestowed upon the Metropolitan Museum of Art in New York at the time of his death.

Jules Bache, like many others of great wealth, usually managed to get his own way, no matter how outrageous the means. In 1936 he travelled to London, England, to see the coronation of King George VI. Fruitlessly searching for a suitable vantage point along the route of the Royal procession, he purportedly feigned a heart attack, took over the entire wing of a hospital that faced the street, and invited friends to share with him one of the best views of the event.

At the end of August, 1938, Bache returned on the *Normandie* from one of his frequent trips to Europe. It was just before the Munich crisis over the Nazi takeover of the Sudetenland province of Czechoslovakia. A *Wall Street Journal* reporter asked him if he thought there would be war. "They are all bluffing," Bache scoffed. "Hitler is the biggest bluffer over there, and he is getting away with it." But in 1939, on a trip abroad with his good friend, Col. John MacLean of Toronto, he visited the German border. What he saw and heard there changed his mind: he became convinced that war was imminent.

Bache appreciated his privacy, but often entertained at home or at his Camp Wenonah up at Saranac Lake, New York. Occasionally he would rent a railway car to take a group of friends for several sun-filled days at the camp.

During his lifetime, Bache never lost his admiration for beautiful women and was known as a dapper and bemonocled *habitué* of the gayer night spots. On Sundays he often went with his family for dinner to Luchow's, a famous New York restaurant, after which he would depart for the burlesque house across the street. In 1944, after a serious illness landed him in a Palm Beach hospital, he reportedly showed sure signs of recovery by chasing the nurses along the corridors.

Bache was a keen and astute businessman and had numerous other business connections, among which was the Chrysler Corporation in which he had a large shareholding and served as Vice-President. He also figured prominently in the merger of the old Tennessee Company and Cities Service.

When this notable figure died at the age of 83, many were concerned about Dome's future. They had little need to worry because, as the *Wall Street Journal* reported at the time Bache relinquished his presidency, "he desired to transfer the active detailed direction to younger hands, in order to ensure continuity of the policies which he established." Bache was confident that his goals for Dome would be vigorously upheld by Clifford W. Michel, his grandson-in-law, de-

*Alex Fasken at his law office
desk in Toronto.*

spite some initial opposition to the youthfulness of the new leader from the fiery Alexander Fasken.

Bryce MacKenzie, then a young lawyer in Fasken's firm and an Assistant Secretary of Dome, found Alex Fasken to be a strangely contradictory man, "very generous in many ways, niggardly in others." As a law student, MacKenzie was once hard up (as most students still are), and approached Fasken for help, who responded immediately and generously by doubling MacKenzie's stipend from $5 to $10 per week. The Dome Secretary was also generous "when one really didn't need the generosity," MacKenzie said. Although refusing to pay students articling with his firm for the gowns they had to wear for the graduation ceremonies at Osgoode Hall, he would, without question, pay for the much more expensive silk gown required by established members of the firm on being granted the distinction of King's Counsel.

Fasken had a "strong ego," MacKenzie recalled, an opinion shared by many others. He was a short, wiry man with a low boiling point that often hindered his career despite his vast knowledge. John Robinson, hired by Fasken as a law student and eventually appointed as an Assistant Secretary of Dome, remembered him as "a bit of a martinet — when he yelled, we jumped." Despite these human frailties that did not always endear him to his subordinates, Fasken was a man of great ability and devotion who served both the legal profession and the Company with diligence and integrity. In his tribute to Jules Bache and Alex Fasken, Joe Stovel said fittingly, "They were the dominant personalities in the Company structure. Dome Mines was exceedingly fortunate to have two such men at the helm over most of its life."

Dome also considered itself fortunate in having had Stovel in a managerial position for so many years. He was the driving force in the Dome mining operation, and when Sigma also became his responsibility, he assumed that additional burden with equal efficiency and effectiveness.

Joe Stovel concerned himself at all times with the well-being of the mine's families. In *A Mining Trail, 1902-1945,* Stovel related his efforts to obtain better housing for some of these families:

> At the time Dome was started, homes were built for the staff members in the plant area. When Dome Extension was bought, a village, also called Dome Extension, was built for some of the workmen. They were supplied with lake water (not too good) for general purposes, and drinking water came from a nearby well. There were, too, other groups of houses, not too good, in the vicinity of the mine and a veritable shack town, on Company land, had grown up. It was called Little Italy . . .
>
> After we bought the Schumacher claims and were making extra

money, I asked to be allowed to use some of this to do away with Little Italy. That was granted, and I built more homes at Dome Extension. Then the owners of homes at Little Italy were given the option of renting a home at Dome Extension or of moving their shacks off our property. Very few of them moved the homes to South Porcupine, the majority taking homes at Dome Extension. So Little Italy was a thing of the past . . . I supposed it was the effect of so many employees living on the property that gave Dome employees unusual unity. In sports, or in anything else, it was Dome against the rest of the (Porcupine) camp.

Stovel also extended his interests outside the mine to community affairs. After serving for six years on the public school board, he resigned in order to join the Board of the South Porcupine Hospital and was appointed Chairman "almost in one motion," he said. The old hospital, a veritable firetrap in Stovel's opinion, was to be replaced by a new one with plans drawn by a local architect which were, although "very pretty, not what we needed nor within our possible price range." He then spent several days in Toronto, learning as much as possible about hospitals and building regulations from provincial health and public works officials. "Then back to the mine, where I got a staff draughtsman to draw a floor plan. The only thing I forgot was an ambulance entry and a receiving room," he said proudly. After these were added, the rough plan was handed to the architect, who reluctantly drew new plans.

Funds were now needed to carry out construction of the new building. The Dome Board contributed the site for the hospital and $25,000, and were joined, unasked, by Hollinger and McIntyre, who each donated $5,000. Altogether, due largely to Stovel's persistence, $100,000 was raised, including $50,000 from Fred Schumacher, Dome's nemesis. Needing $10,000 more for a nurses' residence, Stovel was able to persuade the provincial government to foot the bill. Work began in mid-August, 1937, and the hospital was opened six and a half months later.

During the Second World War, Stovel served as Chairman of a newly formed chapter of the Red Cross Society at South Porcupine. He also arranged that Dome would match the amount raised by its employees for a Dome War Charities Fund. Stovel was particularly proud of Dome's fringe benefits programme, such as a non-contributory group life insurance plan established in 1925, which included a total disability benefit for men under the age of 60. Five years earlier, a "fairly generous" sick pay plan, also non-contributory, had been set up which provided for the payment of 50 per cent of an employee's wages, for up to six months, during absences from work due to illnesses or non-occupational accidents. (The Workmen's Compensation Board's benefits covered accidents that occurred on the job.) An optional medical and hospital care plan, providing specific services, was made available to workers for a fee of $1.50 a month — long before the introduction of the Ontario Health Insurance Plan. Stovel said with great satisfaction: "We were always a step ahead of the other mines in these matters." Another first for Dome, for which Stovel is given credit, was the establishment in 1937 of a pension plan:

> It fell to my lot, as General Manager, to first suggest and finally to have the Company set up a pension scheme. Bob Dye was a great help to me in this. We were starting something that no gold mine in Ontario had and we had to fight resistance from inside as well as outside.
>
> At that time we looked up all the data we could get our hands on and the only mining pension that we could discover in Ontario was the one in effect at the International Nickel Company. On our Board, Mr. Bache left the matter up to the Board. Alex Fasken was the only Director favouring it at first. Without his fighting spirit I don't think we could have won out. The rest of the Board were indifferent or violently opposed. It took two years to get a favourable decision . . . The scheme was not as generous as we could have wished but it was all we thought that we could get. As a starter, to cover years of back service, the Board had to put $545,000 in the fund . . . I am very proud of starting that — prouder of it than of anything I did at Dome.

The non-compulsory pension scheme was open to employees upon the completion of two years of service, who paid approximately one-third of the cost with the Company picking up the balance. Since 1973, the Company has paid the full cost of the original plan. From the commencement of the various plans to December 31, 1981, the Company has paid $8,213,707, or 75 per cent of the total cost, and the employees have paid $2,765,528.

At this time as well, a public health nurse was engaged for full-time employment, supplementing the duties of the first-aid attendant, who tended to the minor sicknesses of employees and their families and to the light injuries that occurred on the job. For many years, a Company physician has lived on the mine property in a residence which, in the early days before the hospital, housed a 12-bed clinic.

After his "retirement" in 1945, Stovel held the title of Vice-President until 1956, during which time he was Managing Director for seven years and retained as a consultant for an additional four years.

Dome held first place in the affections of Joe Stovel, who believed that the mine would have a long and prosperous future, despite the dire predictions of many critics. "Many years ago," he said in the late fifties, "I publicly stated that I would be pushing up the daisies before Dome was finished. I still think so . . . Dome was and is a wonderful mine."

CHAPTER 13

Progressing into Prosperity

A side effect of the Second World War was a period of serious inflation in the North American economy. This proved detrimental for the gold mining industry, whose hardwon profits, already restricted by the fixed price for its product and the grave shortage of labour, were eroded by rapidly depreciating dollars.

These were difficult times for Dome, perhaps the most difficult in the Company's history. *The Northern Miner*, on December 28, 1944, sympathetically summed up the situation under the headline, DOME AT LOW EBB BUT HANGS ON:

> This has not been a happy year for Dome Mines Limited. Production, earnings, dividends, have fallen to the lowest in many years, and difficulties have risen to a new high for the war period. Yet there's a silver lining. Results might have been worse; that they weren't under the disabilities suffered is a sign of the inherent good health of the mine, and the best possible witness of what the performance will be when good times come back for gold mining people. Despite the low level to which performance has fallen as a result of an insufficiency of labour to keep it up, the organization established on and around Dome is seen to contain the things upon which can be erected greater results in the future than were ever had in the past.

Although less ore was being treated, the tonnage milled had "held up remarkably well," being only 16 per cent below the record set in 1940. "It's a good performance," the paper commended, "and could only have been accomplished by a crew of excellent and loyal workers."

Dome had also managed to maintain the quantity and grade of its ore reserves. As old areas were mined out, "unexpected additions to the known bodies and unsuspected subsidiary orebodies made their appearance . . . (but) the area of the mine upon which work is focused is now pretty well carved up. There is not the same room for new chances, nor are the miners available for the needed development and exploration work."

It was believed that Dome would need at least two years after the end of the war as a period of rehabilitation, since production was not expected to be normal and costs were certain to rise. There was, however, a bright side:

> The main mine, which has been producing for a third of a century, doesn't look to be more than halfway through its life — thanks to a policy which gathered five miles of ground in its rich Porcupine neighbourhood, of which 3½ miles are on the strike of the Dome ore zone.

These properties included Dome Extension, Foley O'Brien, some Goldale claims, Temiskaming, Townsend Veteran, Buffalo Tisdale, Central Porcupine, mining rights under Porcupine Lake and, of course, Schumacher — all "links in a chain assuring safety and security of investment," said *The Northern Miner*. (Others have since been added, making a total of 3,579 acres in Tisdale, Whitney and Shaw Townships in 1982.)

Only a year after assuming the leadership of Dome Mines, Cliff Michel faced the Company's lowest point: death had taken both the Chairman of the Board and the Secretary; the General Manager had retired; tonnage was down to 1,450 per day; and, although victory was in sight, war still raged. Happily for Dome, at least some of these clouds were lifted later in the summer of 1945, with the end of hostilities in both Europe and the Far East. Of the 367 workers who had enlisted, 218 had returned to their jobs at Dome by the end of 1946. They, along with the solid corps of older, experienced workers who had remained on the job throughout the war, would give Dome the best work force it had ever had. "There is no finer body of men working for anybody," Stovel praised. In his report for 1945, Michel stated that " . . . (the returning employees) are taking hold in a most satisfactory manner . . . Thus, what was the greatest handicap to our operations during recent years — namely, a lack of labour — is being gradually overcome." Because of this, Dome could put into operation the long-postponed plans for development and expansion of the promising regions to the northeast, and deeper areas within the mine.

President Michel looked ahead to the immediate postwar years with concern, however:

> We have reason to believe that we are entering upon a period which will be more favourable to the gold mining industry than the war years through which we have passed. On the other hand, the tremendous cost of this war with the concurrent increase in national debts will inevitably bring about a higher level of prices, and hence of costs throughout the world . . .
> In this period of shortage of workmen, coupled with rising costs

generally, the problem of the gold mining industry is particularly difficult owing to the fixed selling price for its product — gold . . .

You may be assured we shall continue our unceasing attempts to improve operations and lower costs. However, as income taxes are a major component of any mine's cost, it is to be hoped that governments will more fully appreciate "the wasting asset" feature of mining, if this industry is to make its appropriate contribution to the production expansion that the country and the world need.

The establishment of parity in the exchange rate between the United States' and Canadian dollars in mid-1946 proved to be detrimental to the gold mining industry in Canada, as it effectively reduced the price paid for gold by the Canadian Mint by 10 per cent. Michel stated:

To this Company, this action meant an immediate reduction in operating profit as well as a decline in the value of and the income received from its holdings in other Canadian mines and in its holdings in the dollar and sterling areas; to the marginal mines of Canada it meant operating loss and eventual close-down; to all mines it meant a loss of some portion of their ore reserves.

Michel said that it was "not readily apparent" why this measure had been adopted, adversely affecting, as it did a country whose "prosperity is linked to exports and whose mining industry has acted as a balance wheel in its economy." There was, however, some evidence that the government recognized "the plight in which the industry has been placed and it may reasonably be hoped that, in due course, it will afford relief." Until then, "all that could be done was to run the business in as sound and economical a way as possible."

Four months later, Michel told shareholders that development and maintenance, which had been deferred during the war, was now being carried out as economically as possible and within the framework of a 10 cents per hour wage increase granted by Dome in December. Despite the conscious effort to cut other costs, Dome's net profit for 1946 declined by almost a quarter of a million dollars, a direct result of the revised exchange rate.

Some relief arrived at the beginning of 1947, although not to the extent required by the gold mines to recover from the wartime setbacks. The federal government soon realized that the official fixed price for gold and the adjusted exchange rates would, in Michel's words, "all but destroy the domestic gold mining industry, which not only creates the medium with which Canada's deficit with the United States must be settled, but which is also a stabilizing factor in the country's economy in time of deflation." The government therefore granted an increase in the depletion allowance, a deduction from taxable income which recognized the gradual exhaustion of the mine's principal asset, the ore deposit, and promised additional help from the measures contained in the Emergency Gold Mining Assistance Act then before Parliament.

The EGMA Act, as it was known, was of vital concern to the mining communities as it was intended to slow the closing down of the gold mining industry, thereby allowing time for the development of alternate employment in these areas. First proclaimed in 1948, it continued in force until 1976, due in large part to the efforts of the Town of Timmins Department of Industries and its chairman, J.V. Bonhomme. Over the years, many well-documented submissions advocating continuance of the Act were presented to the government which pointed out the beneficial effects on the communities involved and the national economy. Although the number of operating gold mines in Canada gradually declined from 146 in the war years to 23 in the late seventies, there was minimal disruption to these communities. Total Canadian gold production was reduced by one half, from 3.5 to 1.7 million ounces annually, during the period EGMA was in force. A large number of the gold mines that now contribute so greatly to the wealth of Canada would not be in existence were it not for the assistance received during the difficult years of the fifties and sixties.

For the Dome Mines group in particular, steady employment was provided for more than 1,500 persons, whose personal income taxes in the aggregate were substantial, with a total of $28,892,845 in assistance received from 1949 to 1971 on production of 9,182,346 ounces, an average of $3.15 per ounce. Although this was essential for the survival of Dome and Sigma, wage increases were far greater, and corporate income and mining taxes alone totalled more than $35 million. It is also noteworthy that during the nine-year period following the last receipt of EGMA, corporate income and mining taxes paid by the Dome Mines group totalled $250,446,000.

Increased costs, coupled with the drop in the price of gold since 1939, reduced profits for Dome in 1947 and 1948. Dividend payments were cut substantially, and Michel attributed the decline in profit to three factors: the spiralling cost of materials, higher wages, and increased development work, which had been postponed for many years because of the shortage of labour. Michel also pointed out that, because assistance under EGMA was linked to cost per ounce, it would have a more beneficial effect for producers less efficient than Dome.

For profits to improve, Michel said, either operating costs would have to decrease or the selling price of gold would have to increase. Since the first was unlikely to occur in the short term, the second alternative must be considered:

. . . As to the revaluation of gold, the price of it, where free markets exist – beyond the jurisdiction of the International Monetary Fund – is well above the official price at which mines must sell, reflecting the decline in the value of paper currencies compared with their pre-war purchasing power. The managers of the Fund necessarily try to limit such transactions, which mirror the people's disbelief in the validity of the high exchange rates which the Fund arbitrarily established. Such a course, which appears wholly uneconomic, can continue only as long as the United States is willing to underwrite the cost, and perhaps end only when the pressures of a buyers' market and falling prices reveal the extent to which the managed currencies and artificially high exchange rates have restricted world trade.

During these developments, Dome's newest subsidiary, Dome Exploration (Canada) Limited, was rapidly increasing its exploration activities. In its first year of operation, the Company examined 19 properties, four of which were optioned in 1945, bringing the total under option to 11. Campbell Red Lake appeared to have the most potential, producing "significant" gold values only 1,500 feet south of an old find. Dome Exploration was also diamond drilling 600 feet west of the Campbell Red Lake boundary on the optioned property of Dexter Red Lake Gold Mines Limited, and prospecting on the Bambrick-Beauchemin property in Louvicourt Township of northwestern Quebec where "fair gold values" had been found. In the summer of 1947, exposures of massive sulphides were discovered in the Bachelor Lake area of Quebec. An extensive diamond drilling programme during the next four years indicated a relatively small orebody of 365,000 tons to the 600-foot horizon with a grade of 13.55 per cent zinc, 0.88 per cent lead, and 10.50 ounces per ton silver. As the base metal prices were depressed at that time, all work was suspended until an all-weather road had been constructed into the area by the Quebec government. In August, 1955, rather than develop it themselves, Dome elected to sell the property to Coniagas Mines Limited in return for 500,000 shares of Coniagas stock. Brought into production in 1961 on a 350-tons per day basis, it operated for the next six years.

In 1948, Dome ventured into a field that was new to most of its people: the search for oil in western Canada. This step would have an important bearing on the future course of Dome and began with the acquisition of a small interest in Western Minerals Limited and its affiliate, Western Leaseholds Limited. By the end of 1949, these two companies held 488,000 acres of land in the province of Alberta and full interest in 40 producing oil wells in the Redwater field, as well as royalty interests in 18 wells in the famous Leduc field.

That year Dome organized another subsidiary, Dome Exploration (Western) Limited, to bid on proven and semi-proven oil acreage. To finance the new Company's operations, Dome committed itself to the expenditure, in instalments, of $2,500,000. Dome decided, however, that the risks of oil exploration should be spread over a larger pool of venture capital and arranged for the subscription of an additional $7,500,000 to Dome Exploration (Western) by outside interests, which included three investment trusts and two independent oil companies. Dome was now well on its way to active participation in the search for oil in the West, with Jim McCrea as the Vice-President responsible for all mineral and hydrocarbon exploration. The enterprise would later grow into the internationally known Dome Petroleum Limited, the history of which, although fascinating, is lengthy and not directly related to mining, and therefore not included in this volume.

The death in 1946 of Senator Alex D. McCrae, who had served as a major-general in the Canadian Army in the First World War, left a vacancy on the Board of Directors, which was filled the next year by Major-General A. Bruce Matthews, C.B.E., D.S.O., Vice-President and Treasurer of the Excelsior Life Insurance Company of Toronto.

Robert E. Dye replaced Joe Stovel upon his retirement as General Manager in 1944. Shortly after accepting the post, his General Superintendent, W.H. Johns, an employee of the Company for a quarter of a century, died suddenly of a heart attack. Fortunately, there was a well-qualified replacement at hand — Charles P. Girdwood, who had been with Dome for eight years and had held the post of Chief Mining Engineer for the previous five years.

As the forties drew to a close, management looked back at the past decade with mixed feelings. Half war and half peace, the years saw problems arising from the war that overshadowed what should have been a prosperous time. But, despite the setbacks, the loss of key personnel and economic problems, the Dome organization, with its new and youthful management, was in a position at the beginning of the fifties to take advantage of opportunities that lay ahead. Sigma was now well established, the new Campbell Red Lake mine was a most promising producer, and Dome Exploration (Western) was moving rapidly into the exciting new fields of oil and natural gas.

CHAPTER 14

The Campbell Red Lake Mine

The story of Red Lake dates back to 1872, when a government geologist undertook a preliminary geological survey of the district and found a zone consisting mainly of volcanic and intrusive rock, formations likely to contain gold-bearing ore. The first recorded prospecting effort was carried out by the Northwestern Ontario Exploration Company in 1887, but gold was not discovered until 1922. The promoters of this strike, Herbert Tyrell and Fred Carroll, encountered financing problems and were forced to relinquish their claims. In 1925 Lorne Howey and George McNeeley staked claims on what eventually became the area's first producer, the Howey Mine, which began production in 1930 and remained active for eleven years. Several others were later brought into production, such as Madsen, McKenzie, Dickenson, and Cochenour-Willans, but the biggest of them all was the Campbell Red Lake Mine.

The Campbell claims, located in Balmer Township two miles east of Red Lake, were first staked by Edward Derraugh for the Summers-Derraugh Syndicate on February 28, 1926. Gordon G. Summers, an Ontario Land Surveyor from Haileybury, was one of the principals and also a Director of Hulroy Mines Limited at Haileybury, a company to which the registered claims were turned over. Surface prospecting and sampling were carried out during the summers of 1926 and 1927 but the results were disappointing and the claims were cancelled on June 8, 1928. That same day these claims were restaked by Colin A. Campbell.

The Campbell family was well known in prospecting circles. George, John and Clifford Campbell, three brothers, and their cousin, Colin, had all been prospecting for a number of years, and Clifford had been a member of the Dome 1909 party which staked one of the richest gold claims in the Porcupine. George Campbell was especially well known for his gregarious personality and his practical jokes. A true prospector of the "old school," he was once hired by the Howey mine to take young geologists and engineers on field trips. After a few of these trips he came home one night and groused to his wife, "Oh, I've had it with these geologists — they've got book learning and they're so stupid it makes me sick. They know their ore when it's oxidized on the bench, but show 'em that same ore that's brought out from underground and they don't know one thing from another."

One of George's many antics took place when he was about 21 years of age, when he and a friend were asked to drive 1,000 horses, on a C.O.D. basis, from Belgium to the Pyrenees Mountains for the Spanish government. The pair started out, stopping every so often for "refreshment" in the little villages along the way, financing their travels by selling a few horses here and there. By the time they finally reached the Pyrenees Mountains, only two horses were left. They explained to the Spanish government that the other 998 had died from a mysterious ailment along the way, and by the time the officials found out what had actually happened, George and his buddy were safely back in Canada.

Back in Red Lake, much interest was taken in a promising zone of rhyolite, basic lava and sedimentary rocks south of Balmer Lake, but many a prospector would come and go during the next sixteen years before any real action was to take place. The Campbells cancelled their No. 360 and No. 361 claims in the area on October 25, 1928, after which they were worked for a time by Joseph Prena, a prospector from Hearst, Ontario. No significant gold values were uncovered and in the spring of 1931 they were again cancelled. By this time George Campbell was working with Prena and they decided to concentrate their efforts on claim No. 358, on the south shore of Balmer Lake, a claim which Prena held until his death in 1939.

No. 361, the key claim and the site of the present mine and mill, remained open until 1938 at which time it was restaked by Mrs. Marion Harper. Campbell was hired to carry out the assessment work but, once again, no gold values were found and in 1940 the claim changed hands again. It was restaked in May, 1944, by Colin Campbell, who had already staked nine claims to the south. George Campbell restaked Prena's old claim, No. 358, and two others to the east.

Visible gold had been discovered in drill cores about 800 feet north of the present Dickenson Red Lake Mine east of the Campbell claims. Now optimistic, the two cousins decided to move quickly. In July they travelled to Toronto with their partner, A.K. McLeod, to consult Willard M. Gordon, their lawyer, and to meet with John M. Brewis and Arthur W. White, Toronto stockbrokers and mining promoters of considerable reputation. A deal was concluded on the strength of surface showings and Campbell Red Lake Mines Limited was incorporated by letters patent dated July 18, 1944. The officers were Arthur M. White, President; John M. Brewis, Vice-President and Managing Director; Willard M. Gordon, Secretary; John M. Rudd and Charles H. Gordon, Directors. The firm of Brewis and White Limited put up $10,000 in return for 1.2 million of the 3.5 million $1 par value shares and took options on the remainder. From the 1.2 million shares, 200,000 were set aside for delivery as a bonus to buyers of treasury stock on the basis of one share for each ten bought. A total of 700,000 shares was taken up under the option, providing an additional $65,000 for the treasury; thus $75,000 was raised for surface exploration to be carried out that summer and fall.

George Campbell returned to Red Lake and began trenching with the help of Jacob Hager and his sons, William and Elderidge, three Ojibway Indians. They discovered two quartz veins which gave high assays over narrow widths, and Campbell brought in Harvey Kendrick of McKenzie Island, Red Lake, to drill several shallow holes for blasting. The trench was deepened to eight feet and small quantities of gold were again found.

On September 28, 1944, an advertisement was placed in *The Northern Miner* by Brewis and White, extolling the investment opportunity at Campbell Red Lake and describing the property as having "extraordinary merit and most outstanding possibilities." At this time, geological mapping of the Red Lake district, begun in the late nineteenth century, was completed under the direction of Dr. H.C. Horwood of the Ontario Department of Mines. This detailed material was no doubt of great help to James McCrea, then General Manager of Sigma Mines, in that it supplemented his own considerable knowledge of the area's geology, gained from his early work as a geologist with the Department mapping in the Red Lake area. After careful consideration, McCrea decided that the claim group deserved a thorough investigation and on November 7, 1944, a deal was concluded with Brewis and White whereby Dome could eventually control 57 per cent of the outstanding capital of Campbell Red Lake Mines Limited. Dome initially acquired 100,000 shares for $25,000 and took options on a further 1,900,000 treasury and issued shares.

George Campbell's wife, Gene, recalled: "After the Campbell mine was staked, everything from here to the Arctic Circle was staked . . . Brewis and White didn't think Campbell was as good as Dickenson so they took Dickenson."

George Campbell had retained Gordon R. Bradshaw, a consulting mining engineer, to survey the claims and make recommendations on further work. In a report dated July 1, 1944, Bradshaw suggested that "the old trenches be widened and cleaned out, that further surface work be done and that a serious effort be made to trace the shear" which was found on the adjoining Craibbe-Fletcher claims. It was later reported that the Campbells had discovered "visible gold over a substantial width . . . values appeared high and the trench had been extended for a distance of 20 feet across the vein with no wall on the south as yet." As it was already late in the year, quarters were built in preparation for a winter drilling programme to begin in January of 1945.

Morrisette Diamond Drilling Company of Haileybury, Ontario, was contracted by Dome Exploration for a minimum of 3,000 feet of drilling. After holes were spotted by R.A. Shatford, a consulting mining engineer, crews working around the clock drilled 47 holes totalling 29,956 feet by the end of the year, disclosing interesting intersections in an area approximately 900 feet wide and 1,200 feet long. Two promising zones were also discovered about 500 feet apart and striking in a north-west direction. Curiously, none of these finds seemed to be associated with the previously opened-up surface showings. Rock outcrops constituted only four per cent of the land area and the overburden varied in thickness from 40 to 200 feet. To explain this inconsistency, a geophysical survey was carried out in February, 1946, on two claims which proved most encouraging. The first holes drilled in a cross-sectional programme encountered what was probably the richest drill core ever recovered in Canada. Massive gold was exposed over a length of about 30 inches at a depth of 275 feet. "Quite heavy visible gold" was found in other cores and further drilling indicated ore at increased depths. With these exciting results, Dome Exploration decided to embark upon underground exploration.

Dome first exercised its option on 100,000 shares of Campbell Red Lake Mines Limited, then at 25 cents a share, and 100,000 shares at 30 cents a share. Issued capital was 2,300,005 shares, with 1,199,995 shares in the treasury. In the fall of 1945, George Campbell, Colin Campbell and W.M. Gordon resigned, and Campbell Red Lake came under new management, with A.W. White as President, Clifford Michel, Vice-President, C.C. Calvin, Secretary-Treasurer, and J.G. McCrea as General Manager. Horace Young was appointed Mine Manager, followed, in 1948, by Joseph Chisholm, who had been Chief Engineer at Sigma for the previous twelve years. Serving as General Superintendents were R. Gosselin (from 1948 to 1956), James Turner (1957 to 1964), and M.A. Taschereau (1965 to 1970).

The new Directors immediately authorized a development programme which included the sinking of a shaft as soon as machinery could be moved to the property the next spring. The four-compartment shaft, with an initial depth of 600 feet, would be positioned between the north and south zones, about 700 feet from the claim's southern boundary. Road work and site clearing began in the late winter months and the shaft collar was installed, along with a temporary wooden headframe. Sinking began in September with the aid of two portable compressors, and the temporary winter camp was torn down, with construction beginning on permanent quarters for a hundred men, an office, machine shop, warehouse and powerhouse. A visitor to the site, impressed by the durable quality of the concrete foundations and steel structures, surmised that Dome planned on "staying there a long time."

By early March, 1947, the shaft was bottomed at 597 feet, with stations cut at the 175-, 300-, 425-, and 500-foot levels. Surprisingly, a narrow streak of free gold was unexpectedly encountered in a three-foot wide heavily mineralized zone at the 295-foot level, providing further incentive to management. Cross-cutting began immediately on all four levels, and the engineers estimated that the ore zones would be reached within a month's time.

There was tremendous public interest in the venture by this time as rumours about large-scale production plans began to spread. Dome management refrained from making premature estimates of ore reserves, but on June 19, 1947, *The Northern Miner* glowingly described the "jewellery display," with its "spectacularly high grade ore," at the third level south cross-cut. In fact, all four levels proved rich in ore, with underground results exceeding surface drilling indications. At the close of 1947, ore reserves were estimated to be 147,230 tons in place, grading 0.556 ounces of gold a ton, with a further 23,884 tons, averaging 0.368 ounces, stockpiled on the surface. The reserves in place were entirely in the south zone, although underground drilling had also shown good possibilities in both the central and north zones. In view of these excellent results, the decision was made to prepare the mine for production.

The Company had been fortunate that development costs were comparatively low because of the close proximity of the ore zones to the shaft, meaning that not much "dead" work had to be done. In fact, few mines in Canada have had such a high percentage of development work in gold-rich ore. The decision to equip the mine for production, however, entailed costs that were bound to be high because of the site's isolation and post-war problems. The initial estimate of the cost of the mill and necessary working capital was $2 million, assuming a one-year construction period.

In a letter to the shareholders of Campbell Red Lake Mines on October 1, 1947, President A.W. White outlined a financing plan which "involved no major reorganization of the capital structure." He proposed that authorized capital be increased to 3,750,000 shares by the addition of 250,000 shares, and further, that a five-year bond for $1,750,000 be issued, which would bear interest at either four or five per cent and would be repaid out of Campbell Red Lake's first profits. Dome Mines Limited gave a commitment for the entire principal of the bond, for which it received the right "to purchase all or any part of the newly created 250,000 treasury shares at par at any time prior to the redemption of the bond." This arrangement was approved by the shareholders at a special general meeting on November 3, 1947, and the way was clear for the planning and construction of the mill.

The plant, designed by mill consultants Dunn and Dowsett, would employ three methods of treatment: mineral jigs (which concentrate ore on a screen submerged in water by agitation or by pulsation) to recover coarse gold, flotation (whereby some mineral particles are induced to become attached to bubbles and float, leaving the worthles gangue behind) to produce sulphide concentrate, and treatment of the flotation tails in a separate cyanide circuit. Because of the arsenopyrite content of the ore, roasting of the concentrate was found to be necessary to ensure maximum economic recovery. The type of roaster used by the nearby Cochenour-Willans Mines was therefore incorporated into the plans. The mill was designed with a rated capacity of 300 tons a day, which could be increased to 500 tons in the future. Much of the machinery came from another Dome subsidiary, Indian Molybdenum Limited of Preissac Township, Quebec.

In the spring of 1948, work began on the excavation and foundations for the mill, crusher house and the new steel headframe. It soon became evident that access to the site would be a major problem. In 1946, the town of Red Lake had been connected by road to the transcontinental railway lines at Vermilion Bay, but another road was still required to reach the Campbell Red Lake site. The shortest existing route was over three miles of water and one mile of land, which was feasible in winter and summer, but not when the ice was unreliable. Consequently, late in 1948, the Company built a seven-mile winter road with a 300-foot bridge suspended on old hoisting cables over the Chukuni River.

This construction, along with delays in the delivery of steel and supplies, higher than anticipated labour costs, and changes in plant design, resulted in a $600,000 cost overrun. Start-up of the mill, originally scheduled for January, 1949, was also delayed. Underground development, however, continued at a good pace and the new 115-foot steel headframe was built around and over the old wooden one, with minimal interruption of work.

By the spring of 1949, the shaft was bottomed at 1,150 feet, with stations cut for four more levels. In March, cross-cutting began on levels five, six and seven towards the main south ore zone, a distance of 250 feet. At this time, with 200 men working above and below ground, construction of the crusher, ore bins and mill was nearing completion and the roaster building was expected to be ready by August.

On June 1, 1949, what was described as "one of the finest new gold mills ever to be built in Canada" went into operation, soon reaching its rated capacity of 300 tons a day. However, gold shipments for the first three months of operation fell far below expectations. The crusher had to undergo further modifications, so the bulk of the mill feed during this period came from the lower grade surface stockpile. As well, flotation concentrates had to be stored until the roaster went into operation. By September, the initial break-in period had passed and the plant was processing well over 300 tons a day. A portion of the mill feed was being drawn deliberately from the lower grade sulphide zones rather than from the richer but smaller south zone, with the objective of mining an average grade and thereby prolonging the mine's life.

In the Company's annual report for 1949, estimates of ore reserves were again revised upwards to 420,500 tons, an increase of 99,800 tons over the previous year. Priority was now given to opening up the north ore zone at the fifth, sixth and seventh levels, and a renewed diamond drilling programme was underway on the surface; if substantial orebodies could be located within a reasonable distance from the shaft, it would not be necessary to deepen it for many years. In August, 1950, a new vein was encountered on the third level in the south zone about 400 feet southwest of the main vein, thought to be a faulted westerly extension. As well, early in 1951, an entirely new type of orebody with "extremely healthy tonnage possibilities" was opened up about 500 feet north of the shaft, in territory previously believed to be inhospitable, with grade running over $20 a ton. The new orebody was a mineralized zone in an altered band of rock which had not previously yielded ore; free gold was present in well-mineralized blue quartz stringers associated with massive arsenopyrite. By fall, it was estimated that this new find contained approximately 200,000 tons of ore, grading about 0.74 ounces a ton, virtually a mine in itself. The orebody appeared to be a branch structure trending due north from the main north zone (which ran northwest to southeast), raising the possibility that other north-south structures existed, in which case the entire area north of the original north zone would be worth exploring.

On the heels of this development came another major discovery to the west. At the seventh or bottom level, a rich vein was found some 300 feet north of the original south zone, running parallel to it and extending in a northwesterly direction. This vein, about 15 feet in width, averaged one ounce per ton, making it the most promising area of the mine.

At first it was thought that the new north-south orebody would be easier to treat than either of the two original zones, but it proved to be high in arsenopyrite and therefore more difficult. The grade of the south zone improved as it was opened up on the lower levels. While the bulk of the mill feed was drawn from this latter zone, which had a recovery rate of 91 per cent, when combined with ore from other zones, the rate dropped to 89 per cent.

The financial prospects for the Campbell Red Lake operation were most encouraging. The mill had been brought into production at a total cost to Dome Mines of $3,513,880. Funds advanced by Dome under the income bond, totalling $3,043,600 in principal and interest, were repaid within a short three and a half years. The first Campbell Red Lake dividend of $199,975 or 5 cents a share was declared in 1952, which trebled the next year, indicative of the Campbell mine's future prosperity.

Development work continued to uncover new and richer ore and in 1953 the shaft was deepened to 2,150 feet, with seven new levels. The next spring, a spectacular new orebody was discovered lying close to the shaft at the 14th level, the richest vein encountered so far.

Despite these gratifying developments, many problems still faced the industry. Production costs continued to rise steadily, but the price of gold fell to $33.50 an ounce in 1956, due to the increased value of the Canadian dollar. The squeeze was made even more uncomfortable by increases in provincial taxes. As one might expect, the stock market reflected these conflicts, and later that year Campbell stock fell to a four-year low.

Fortunately, the mine's grade improved with depth and, as this richer ore entered the mill flow, revenues rose enough to meet the burden of increased costs. Preparations were made to use hydraulically placed mill tailings as backfill, which would be passed underground through large diameter bore holes drilled from surface to the seventh level. This method was expected to be particularly helpful in mining the widest orebody, which was rather irregular in outline. Cut and fill mining would increase costs slightly, but this would be more than offset by less dilution and more complete extraction of the ore.

At this time, development priority was being given to the increasingly promising "F" zone, the most westerly orebody. At the seventh or 1,000-foot level, the deepest reached on this vein by 1957, continuous ore was found to extend for a distance of 1,300 feet, with an average grade of 0.644 ounces a ton. Early in the following year, the zone was picked up at the end of a long exploration drive westward on the 14th level, a full 1,000 feet below, and about 2,900 feet from the boundary between the Campbell property and the adjoining Craibbe-Fletcher Gold Mines claims. An agreement was reached whereby Campbell Red Lake would undertake an extended drive along the western extension of its "F" zone, with any ore found on the Craibbe-Fletcher property to be milled at the Campbell mill, with profits shared on a 50-50 basis. Campbell was given an option on 2,000,000 unissued Craibbe-Fletcher shares, valued at $800,000 and a further option on 500,000 shares held by New Dickenson Mines and Sylvanite Gold Mines, which would provide effective control if and when exercised. During 1960, more than 8,000 feet of underground drilling, 2,000 feet of surface drilling and 1,500 feet of underground exploration had been completed. Although the Craibbe-Fletcher property had long been highly regarded because of its favourable geology and strategic location, extensive work failed to discover ore, and further development was discontinued.

Meanwhile, Campbell had taken a 20 per cent share interest in a consortium, launching a major exploration programme on its northern boundary, at the H.G. Young Mine. Plans were made to sink a production-size shaft to 750 or possibly 1,000 feet. To further expand its exploration efforts, Campbell also entered into an agreement with Dome whereby it would participate, to the extent of 30 per cent, in all new exploration undertaken by Dome for five years, beginning January 1, 1959.

During the sixties, the Campbell Red Lake mine settled down to a stable pattern of increasing production and earnings and steady operating costs. Because of this and the good grade of ore, the Company became ineligible for benefits under the EGMA Act. Instead of being partially supported by government aid, the moderately sized mine paid substantial taxes into the federal and provincial treasuries. This independent status proved beneficial, however, since it allowed the sale of its gold on a more profitable basis to markets other than the Royal Canadian Mint.

By this time, the town of Red Lake, humming with activity, was barely recognizable as the tiny, thrown-together settlement that Eugenia ("Gene") Campbell faced as a young bride in the late twenties — an experience no doubt shared by many women who left behind the comforts of town living to venture into the Canadian wilderness. Here are her first impressions:

> When we arrived in Red Lake, everyone came to see just what kind of woman George Campbell had brought himself, and if you have ever seen a scared kitten, I was it. I was a young girl from the Prairies, and, although I had contact with a lot of people, the breed of people that you have in a mining town is very different. Everyone helps you out . . . George and his cousin, Colin, had built a beautiful cabin — everything was made out of white pine, and the logs didn't vary ½″ in size. So I came in as a bride into a lovely cabin with everything in it, which belonged to George and Colin. Colin said that now that George was married, he would give his half as a wedding present to me.
>
> Downtown Red Lake stretched for all of 50 feet and that was it. There was a store with rooms upstairs, a post office, a poolroom and a poker den, and a restaurant. There were also about five or six log cabins that belonged to the staff of Howey, and there was a laundry right at the shore run by a Chinaman. There were eight white women and about three hundred men, and where the town is right now used to be moose pasture — wolves would howl at night. If you didn't wear rubber boots you would lose yourself in the mud. There was one little bit of a sidewalk

between the poolroom, the restaurant and the store and that was it.

Not only did the young Mrs. Campbell have to adjust to a new way of life, she also had to contend with a prankish husband:

> In those days the compressor would make a noise — now you don't hear them because they're underground. I asked George what the noise was, and he told me that it was an animal that was called a side-hill gouger. When I asked him what that was, he told me that it was an animal with one set of legs shorter than the other, so that when it walked around the side of a hill, it would be level. And I believed him! Then he also used to scare me about bears. It got so that I'd be too scared to sleep near the window and too scared to sleep on the other side of the bed because it was too close to the door. One morning I went out to the little outhouse, which had no door on it, and I'm sitting there and I look up and scream my head off because there's a bear right in the doorway! George, who had been watching all along, was laughing away.

Typical of life in the early mining communities was the presence of young ladies known as being of "ill repute."

Many, though, had admirable qualities that were generally overlooked by the townspeople, on the basis of their choice of occupation. One such lady was Patsy:

> There was a manager's wife here who decided she was going to get rid of Patsy, because she felt Patsy was a bad influence on the younger generation, so she circulated a petition. In those days we only had one store, where everyone went to shop on Saturdays. This lady reminded me a lot in her actions of Queen Mary of England, and you know how arrogant she was. Well, she came into the store with her petition and she's holding court and everything and then Patsy came in. And one thing I will say — Patsy was a lady, and I mean a lady. Patsy came in and tapped the lady on the shoulder and said, "Mrs. _____, your husband was at my place last night and forgot his flashlight — here it is." That finished the petition then and there . . .
>
> Patsy came up to me one day and said, "I want you to remember, always remember, that when your husband came into my place he came only to drink and play the piano," — she had the only piano in town. "My girls never ever made advances to men who came to drink. Your husband would drink and play the

"The safest mine in Ontario."
(above)

Campbell Red Lake property
at Balmertown. (below)

piano and entertain us all night. I want you to always remember that." To me she was a lady — she did an awful lot of charity that nobody knew about until these people who had accepted this charity — boys and girls — told others. She put two or three boys through school who became geologists, but the average human being is so narrow-minded that they wouldn't look at a woman like Patsy. She was a very well-educated woman — a graduate of the University of Saskatchewan and a high school teacher for many years. Whatever happened to her in her life that she became a madam, nobody stopped to look into. As far as they were concerned, she was a woman of ill repute and they certainly advertised that, but they never advertised the good things she did.

By the late sixties, the spectre of inflation began to take its toll on the Campbell mine's profits and the future was less predictable. A change in management also occurred when, in 1969, Joseph Chisholm retired after 21 years as Manager and later as General Manager. He was replaced by George E. Peacock, who was transferred from Sigma. Malcolm Taschereau, General Superintendent at Campbell since 1965, was moved to Sigma and replaced by Stewart M. Reid.

Over the next few years, the Campbell mine's employees were proud of winning the Ontario Regional Ryan Trophy, in recognition of the mine's enviable safety record, four times: in 1968, 1969, 1970 and 1972. Justly pleased with this achievement, a sign was erected at the mine's entrance which proclaimed, "SAFEST MINE IN ONTARIO."

Several factors contributed to a decline in profits in the late sixties: a lower international gold price, a lower premium on the U.S. dollar, increasing operating costs because of the general pressure of inflation on wages and supplies, and increased taxes. In 1971 the picture improved somewhat with a higher gold price on the free market.

Growing environmental concerns also began to have an effect on operations. Due to its arsenopyrite content, the gold ore had to be roasted to ensure an efficient gold recovery and emission of gaseous and particulate byproducts was cause for concern. For this reason, the Company embarked on a $1 million programme to improve the roaster plant. The new installations included an electrostatic precipitator and bag filter to treat the roaster effluent, as well as a carbon circuit to recover any gold in the precipitator dust, of which there was a considerable tonnage on hand. Initially, the arsenic trioxide from the new installation was permanently sealed off in a totally enclosed and abandoned dry section of the mine until later, when a market was found for the product.

Apart from the beneficial environmental effects, these improvements contributed to a higher rate of gold recovery.

For years, wages in gold mining had been well below those in the rest of the mining industry, simply because the mines could not afford to pay the rates prevalent in the base metal mines. With the steady rise in gold prices in 1973, however, several gold industry wage contracts began to tie hourly rates to the world market price. At Campbell Red Lake, a combination of these wage increases and environmental protection measures was mainly responsible for the rise in operating costs to $17.11 a ton, as opposed to $9.98 in 1966. Further substantial wage increases and continuing inflation in 1974 contributed to a 19 per cent increase to $20.35 a ton.

The improved market picture, resulting from the establishment of the "two-tier" gold pricing system in 1968, had a favourable impact upon the primary gold producers, with net profits rising dramatically within a few years. In 1972, for example, Campbell Red Lake's net profit almost doubled over the previous year, to $4,667,344. This occurred again the next year, when net profit skyrocketed to $8,908,451. Underground exploration continued at a vigorous pace. Deep exploratory drilling began in 1972 in an attempt to locate the western extension of the west zone, one of the most prolific orebodies in the mine. Even with high gold prices, the rising cost of labour, already abnormally high because of the narrow and irregular orebodies, and increased income taxes began to affect profits. In 1973, the Ontario Mining Tax doubled to $1,810,000, while income taxes rose to $4,125,000. These charges, along with higher operating costs, produced a drop in net earnings for the first nine months of 1974 compared to the previous year, with the London price of gold climbing sharply in the fall, reaching $195 an ounce by December. In 1976, however, the price of gold fell to $140 an ounce at the year's end, recovering to $165 by the end of the next year.

In 1975 Campbell suffered a great loss in the sudden death of George Peacock, General Manager since 1970. He was succeeded by Stewart Reid, and General Superintendents were Allan Ludwig from 1975 to 1978 and Keith Newman since 1979.

Over the next few years, the Company's net income kept pace with the spectacular rise in the price of gold, reaching a high in 1980 of $57,523,000, when gold rapidly rose to a peak of U.S. $850 an ounce on January 21st, with an average price of $719 Can. received for the year. Since those heady days, gold has been considerably lower in value and in 1982 held in the range of U.S. $297 to $450.

Campbell Red Lake continued to broaden its horizons by taking part in aggressive exploration in Ontario and Quebec, as well as in the United States and Alaska. On January 1, 1977, Campbell's portion of Dome's exploration expense was changed to 50 per cent of all Ontario projects and to 40 per cent of all projects outside Ontario and Quebec. However, Campbell still retained the previous 21 per cent interest in projects begun between January 1, 1969, and January 1, 1977. More recently, a $10.4 million expansion programme undertaken in 1979 increased tonnage 22 per cent to 370,000 tons for 1981. Gold production is expected to rise 15 per cent to 212,000 ounces in 1982. The Campbell mine also participated with Dome and Amoco Canada Petroleum Company Ltd. in the development of the Detour Lake gold property, which is covered in a later chapter.

Over the years, the Red Lake district has become one of Canada's foremost gold producing areas, and the tiny, muddy settlement of Red Lake first seen by Gene Campbell is now a modern community of two thousand residents. Although many mines have come and gone over the camp's brief history, A.L. Reading, in a poem entitled, "The New Road to Red Lake," prophesied:

> . . . Some producing mines are proving up
> But Prospectors are not too bright;
> For as time has passed, the efforts wane
> Though there's many a muskeg underlain
> With untold riches in hidden vein
> Which drilling may bring to light.
> But a Prospector has only time to spend
> Who else will share the cost
> The camp is BIG; the formation right;
> There must be a hundred mines in sight
> But they can't be developed overnight
> It takes money and lots of time.

CHAPTER 15

Approaching Fifty Years

At the beginning of the fifth decade since the South Porcupine claims were first staked, the operations of the Dome organization stretched from the new oil fields of Alberta, through two regions of Ontario and into northwestern Quebec, and were soon to touch the Atlantic at Cape Breton Island. The Big Dome itself had been conservatively and efficiently managed, becoming a steady producer that consistently returned profits and dividends in spite of difficult economic conditions, with Campbell Red Lake and Sigma being prolific contributors to Dome's overall success.

In the early fifties, there were signs that Dome's venture into the oil and gas industry, then beginning to thrive in Alberta, would be rewarding. Dome Exploration (Western) held land, mostly in the rich Redwater field, with reserves of 19 million barrels of recoverable oil. The oil cost 30 cents a barrel to develop, and the selling price in 1950 was a profitable $2.70, less one-eighth as a royalty. It was not surprising, then, that *The Northern Miner* regarded Dome with high favour and did not hesitate to convey these feelings to the public. A Brazilian reader sent this inquiry to the editor in March, 1950: "I am shortly going to buy more golds and would appreciate a word from you regarding what you consider are the three best dividend payers which also hold great scope for appreciation." *The Northern Miner's* reply would have pleased the public relations director of any corporation:

> Owing to the far-flung distribution of the shareholders, the profitable character of its operations, and the aggressiveness of its management, Dome Mines is regarded by many observers as the wheel-horse of the gold group . . . Comment upon the company's dividend-paying ability is unnecessary, although this may have been a factor in the shares heading the brokers' poll recently conducted by *The Northern Miner*. The stock was favoured as having the best possibilities of appreciation of any seasoned Canadian mining stock.

One of Dome's few disappointments was Mindamar, an old zinc-lead-copper property which lay 40 miles south of Sydney, on Cape Breton Island in Nova Scotia. On this site stood the Stirling mine, which had been in business for many years, but had closed during the depression of the thirties. Dome Exploration (Canada) engineers and geologists decided to investigate the mine, then owned by Mindamar Metals Corporation Limited, which had indicated and probable reserves of 780,000 tons, estimated at 8 per cent zinc, 1.8 per cent lead, 0.9 per cent copper, 2.00 ounces of silver and .03 ounces of gold per ton.

Dome agreed to provide up to $1,750,000, holding 5 per cent bonds to be retired from earnings, and had an option on 1,450,000 shares for $889,997, to be exercised within one year from the start of production. The 600-foot shaft was de-watered, reconditioned, and later deepened to 1,150 feet, and a mill with a daily capacity of 500 tons was erected. James G. McCrea became President of Mindamar Metals, and promptly arranged for the sale of zinc concentrates to the United Kingdom Ministry of Supply for four years, and of copper-lead concentrates for two years.

The Company established a townsite with 64 homes and a school for 80 children of the work force, and the mine began operating in 1952. In its first year, Mindamar produced "at a profitable level," according to Cliff Michel, but "did not measure up to our expectations, and we encountered metallurgical difficulties in maintaining a steady rate of recovery from the different ores fed to the mill." Nevertheless, management was hopeful that "various changes effected" would "result in a better recovery in the year ahead."

The extension of the shaft to depth, and subsequent level development and diamond drilling, showed that the ore had been adversely affected by massive talc alteration and the grade greatly reduced. Ground conditions became progressively worse at depth and in April, 1956, the Mindamar Mine was closed. Mindamar Metals sold the mill to the Arcadia Nickel Corporation for $525,000, and the original lease section, which contained the mine and the underground workings, was sold to one of the vendors when Dome had first taken over the running of Mindamar - Evan T. Donaldson, and a group of his associates.

In 1952, the recreational activities of some of Dome's employees were restricted when fire destroyed the South Porcupine Arena, which Dome had built for the community in 1938.

It was three o'clock on a quiet January afternoon. Jack McCaw, retired foreman of the Dome powerhouse now, at the age of 70, the Arena's ice plant engineer, was watching two teenaged figure skaters practise their intricate art. Suddenly he smelled smoke and, upon investigating, discovered a blaze in a spare room in the basement. He shouted to the skaters to get out, and immediately called the South Porcupine fire department.

The volunteer firefighters responded quickly, but by the time they arrived, the flames were spreading out of control. Fire Chief Doug McLellan called for more help, and reinforcements speedily arrived from nearby Timmins, Schumacher and Whitney.

Louis Pyke (brother of Harry, Dome's manager since 1972) crashed a bulldozer into the dressing room of the Porkies, the South Porcupine hockey team made up almost entirely of Dome workers. Firemen in respirators managed to save most of the team's equipment, but were unable to retrieve the gear of the other teams using the Arena.

About a hundred firemen fought the blaze which, Vic Travis wrote in the *Timmins Press*, "at times threatened to become a holocaust." It was not until just before midnight that an exhausted Chief McLellan and his men finally got the flames under control. Although the rink itself had been saved from serious damage, almost everything else was in ruins: the dressing rooms, the ice-making plant, the badminton court, the upstairs dance floor and the refreshment concession. The leading teams of three hockey leagues were left with nothing but a pile of ice-coated wreckage.

It was later determined that the fire had been caused by a short circuit in the wiring, and resulted in a total loss of $100,000. Travis went on: "That night, the South Porcupine Porkies skated out on the ice at the McIntyre Arena wearing malodorous sweaters combined with new stockings supplied by Clark's Men's Wear (which had also donated gloves and socks to firefighters in need of them). They managed a 3-1 win over the Hollmacs (the Hollinger-McIntyre team), but their success was tempered by the thought that all remaining games would have to be played on the road."

Unfortunately, nothing more could be done at the time for the teams which had lost everything. But, with an insurance settlement and assistance from Dome Mines, the Arena was soon rebuilt with an improved design, and continues to be the centre of organized recreational activity in the South Porcupine district.

Around this time, death took two of Dome's key men, C.W. Dowsett and his son-in-law, Jim McCrea. Dowsett, whose services with Dome had dated from 1915, died in 1952 at the age of 72. A creative man, many of his ingenious inventions had been put to good use by Dome, and Cliff Michel felt that his death was "an immeasurable loss." In September, 1953, McCrea died suddenly at the age of 55, as a result of complications following a bout of pneumonia. "He will be missed by this Company and by the Canadian mining industry at large," said Michel. "Fortunate for us is the fact that his executive ability included, among its many qualities, that of choosing and developing able assistants who are now carrying on the projects which Mr. McCrea initiated." One such assistant was James B. Redpath.

Redpath had won recognition for his work in the development of the Sigma mine, to which he was assigned after 18 months on exploration at the South Porcupine property. After holding just about every managerial position at the Val d'Or mine, he was moved to Toronto, upon McCrea's death, to fill the newly-created position of Executive Vice-President of Dome Mines, and Vice-President of Campbell Red Lake Mines and of Sigma Mines (Quebec) Limited.

It was also at this time that the retirement of Robert E. Dye, General Manager of the South Porcupine mine since 1945, was announced. His replacement as General Manager was Charles P. Girdwood, who had joined the Dome mine as Assistant Engineer, becoming Chief Engineer until his appointment as Superintendent. He was later appointed both a Vice-President and a Director. Arthur D. Robinson, with 21 years' service, was promoted from Mine Superintendent to General Superintendent.

Girdwood was educated in British Columbia, where he attended public schools and Victoria College. After graduating in engineering from McGill University, he worked for seven years on mining properties in British Columbia, Quebec and Ontario before joining the Dome organization in 1939. During his many years with the Company, he took an active part in community affairs and served on the boards of a number of local organizations, including the Porcupine General Hospital. He was also a director and officer of many professional and business groups, such as the Ontario Mining Association, the Mines Accident Prevention Association of Ontario, the Mining Association of Canada, the Canadian Institute of Mining and Metallurgy, the Ontario Hospital Association, the Advisory Council for Mining Engineering of Queen's University, Ontario Northland Railway, Star Transfer Limited, Sigma Mines (Quebec) Limited and Clinton Copper Mines Limited.

Campbell was indeed proving its worth to Dome, with its dividends paid to the Company in 1955, Michel pointed out, "almost one-half of our other income . . . in spite of the fact that the company received no benefits under the Emergency Gold Mining Assistance Act." Campbell is a high grade, low cost per ounce operation, whereas Dome and Sigma are low grade, high cost per ounce producers.

In his review of the year, Michel was happy about the resolution of some of the problems that had long plagued the industry:

> The return of the buyers' markets and the lack of shortages is welcomed by the gold mining industry, which has long suffered from the squeeze of rising costs and a fixed or declining selling price, expressed in Canadian dollars, for its production. While

James B. Redpath

the level of prices has not declined sufficiently to have any important impact on operating profit margins, the pressure of inflation is at least not bearing as hard upon us as it has for the last decade. In this atmosphere we will continue our policy of searching for new properties in the hope of finding profitable replacements for the reserves we are currently mining.

The fixed selling price for gold was always a matter of serious concern for mine operators and Michel's public statement in March, 1956, reflected this: "Until the United States government accedes to the request of other members of the International Monetary Fund to raise the price of gold, there is only one side of the profit picture on which the gold mine operator can bring any pressure to bear, and that is on cost, both in his own efforts or on those of the Canadian government through its Emergency Gold Mining Assistance programme."

To protect the Company and its shareholders against the eventual loss of their raw material, Dome "improved its liquid position," in Michel's words, "with the hope that these assets can be invested in the exploitation of potential commercial ore properties," under the direction of Jim Redpath, now President of Dome Exploration.

"The best thing ever done for Dome," according to the residents, was the provision of an excellent water supply system to the plant and residences on the property. For many years they had had to put up with the original water supply from Porcupine Lake which, while adequate for process water, required heavy chlorination for domestic use, and potable water of acceptable quality had been delivered daily by horse and cart and later by truck. By connecting a two-mile pipeline to the water main supplying the town of South Porcupine and adding a 150,000-gallon reservoir at Dome, the property was provided with good spring water purchased from the municipality. Another side benefit was that it provided a completely independent water supply in case of fire.

Work at the Big Dome progressed as usual – quietly and efficiently. A journalist visiting South Porcupine reported on January 5, 1956:

> "After $200 million, going just as strong as ever."
>
> That in a nutshell is the story of Dome Mines, one of the real pioneer gold producers of Ontario's famed Porcupine camp and which crossed this milestone only a few months ago.
>
> Aside altogether from its sound investments and string of successful subsidiaries (of which the Company's top management may well be proud), the original mine is in wonderful shape, *The Northern Miner* can report following a visit. Grade shows very little change. But with the mill grinding out a record

tonnage, output for the year just closing (1955) will surpass 1954's $5,867,430. And with costs down, earnings in all probability will be bettered. What is perhaps even more important, the Company is replacing the record tonnage that is being mined. And there is every indication that this can continue for many years to come.

'Our objective is to maintain a comfortable ore reserve,' C.P. Girdwood, General Manager, remarked. And by adhering to a steady development pattern, this is being accomplished without too much difficulty, it is gathered. Grade, too, looks very stable. (Last year the Company reported 2,461,000 tons in reserve, or about a 3-½ year supply).

While there are a number of fine new ore developments that would make headline news at a smaller mine, Dome's operators take these in their stride. Such occurrences are just a matter of course at a mine of this stature . . .

And speaking of efficiency, the size of the payroll has been reduced this past year to an average of 920, despite the peak milling rate. This in turn is reflected in a reduction in operating costs.

Nine months later, the *Miner* reported that management was "constantly on the watch for ways and means to improve efficiency and thereby cut costs":

Recent laboratory research work has shown that recovery could be upped somewhat if ore treated by cyanidation was given a longer agitation period. To provide the increased agitation, six Pachuca air agitators are being installed. It is not certain how much improvement will result from the new additions, but the capital expenditures are modest and the gain can be expected to be well worthwhile.

The *Miner* also commented on the extra ore storage capacity which had been planned to keep the mill operating steadily. This was necessary to offset the gradual decrease in working hours from 56 to 48 and finally to 44.

Management did not concern itself solely with production, however, as a *Miner* report entitled "Like Father, Like Son," which appeared in January, 1957, indicates:

It probably falls to the lot of few managements, mining or industrial, to have such an unusual and deserving tribute paid day in and day out to the management of Dome Mines. For certainly there is no other way to describe the fact that father-son combinations account for no less than one-quarter of the

Company's work force. There are, in fact, a total of 114 father-son teams on the payroll, representing 27 per cent of the 900 employees. And this doesn't include another 32 sons whose fathers are either on pension from Dome or were on pension when they died.

Dome has always had happy relations with its employees. Credit for this must largely go to the late General Manager, Robert E. Dye, whose warm friendliness won the heart of every man on the property. The atmosphere that he created lives on after him and is admirably maintained by General Manager C.P. Girdwood . . . the Company's efforts to establish a happy family pay big dividends in developing a force of loyal and stable employees.

Bryce MacKenzie, Assistant Secretary in the fifties and later Secretary, noted that Dome operated for 60 years without a union, and was, in fact, the last mine in the area to be unionized. This was probably because Dome paid five or ten cents an hour more than the neighbouring mines and, in addition, offered its workers a pension plan that at the time was unique in the mining industry. In May, 1969, the United Steelworkers were certified as the bargaining agent for Dome's workers. It was not until a decade later that Dome suffered its first strike, of two weeks' duration, and in 1981 there was another strike which lasted two months. For the most part, however, relations between labour and management have been amicable and mutually satisfactory.

Although Dome had achieved remarkable success in its relations with its employees, its attainment of ideal operational levels was hindered by a chronic lack of sufficient workers. In 1957, Girdwood argued that the answers to the mining industry's need for manpower "are not going to be found in Canada during the present boom conditions." It was his conviction that the industry should put pressure upon the federal government for an easing of the restrictions on immigration, which were then very severe. New policies were eventually adopted which, Girdwood said, would allow the entry into Canada of immigrants "who are badly needed to supplement the work force with men who are able, willing, and adaptable to the productive work that mining affords." From this new source, Dome was able to acquire 41 immigrants from Scotland, England and Northern Ireland for surface and underground employment.

With the parent mine and its subsidiaries now on a steady course, increasing emphasis was placed on exploration. Campbell and Sigma were included in the overall Dome programme for the first time. Michel explained: "We continue to spread our exploration through joint ventures. So as to be able to continue on this course more extensively . . . we propose to enter into a joint exploration agreement with our subsidiaries, Campbell Red Lake and Sigma, whereby they will participate for five years, beginning January 1, 1959, in all new exploration ventures undertaken by Dome." The interests were shared 60 per cent by Dome, 30 per cent by Campbell and 10 per cent by Sigma.

Probably the most important exploration work in which Dome took part during this period was in the Mattagami district near the Quebec-Ontario border. In the late fifties, Karl J. Springer, a veteran prospector-turned-scientific mine finder (and one of the first to use helicopters in mine exploration), persuaded a group of mining companies to join him and his associate, J.M. Richard Corbet, in exploring the Mattagami Lake region. The consortium, known as the Mattagami Syndicate, was composed of Springer's own Leitch Gold Mines, Highland-Bell, Corbet's Area Mines, Dome, Teck-Hughes, and Iso Uranium Mines. Springer and Corbet estimated that the programme they had designed, a broad prospecting project spread over three years, would cost $300,000. Each company took a 16-⅔ per cent interest in the venture.

They worked in a belt of greenstone in a region stretching from the Ontario-Quebec border east through the Waswanipi Lake region and northeast toward Chibougamau. An aerial electromagnetic survey revealed the presence of many anomalies (zones indicating a change of magnetic intensity) in an area of 600 square miles close to Mattagami Lake. Dome Exploration (Quebec) assisted in staking many of these anomalies, including the claims which covered the Mattagami Lake orebody. The first drill hole in June, 1957, produced impressive results, passing through 50 feet of overburden to strike massive sulphides of copper and zinc with gold and silver values.

A large, irregular, replacement-type orebody was discovered on the Watson group of claims, later to become Mattagami Lake Mines. At least 1,000 feet long and, in places, 300 feet wide, the ore reserves were estimated at between 5 and 10 million tons, with an average grade between 10 and 12 per cent zinc. Even at the low metal prices of that time, the sale of the zinc alone would cover the cost of production and the sale of the copper, gold and silver would provide the profit.

Although news from field parties was closely guarded, leaks invariably occurred. This happened in the spring of 1957, when unofficial reports of the early drilling results at Mattagami reached the outside world, precipitating a wild rush of claim stakers. In just a few days, each of the mining recorders at Amos, 75 miles south of Mattagami Lake, and at nearby Val d'Or and Noranda, issued about 500 licenses.

Initial showings were encouraging, but much more drilling was required to determine the structure and size of the orebody. Drilling continued that fall in the Watson Lake area, as well as on 80 claims south of Dunlop Bay on

Mattagami Lake. The ore on the Watson Lake claims at this stage was not completely defined, but indicated grades were consistently high and the orebody eventually proved to be the only one of economic importance found in the area. In fact, Watson Lake was the most significant mineral discovery made in Canada in 1957, a remarkable testimony to the value of scientific methods of exploration.

Before a mine could be established, however, the Mattagami Syndicate faced some serious problems. The only access to the property was by air from Senneterre, about 90 miles northwest, or from Val d'Or, located 125 miles south of the property, and local air services were hard pressed to keep up with the rush. Although the Watson Lake claims were surrounded by muskeg, engineers believed that construction of a railway line, linking up with the main Canadian National track 45 miles away, would be feasible, with substantial amounts of fill.

There was also the problem of power. The Quebec government had been surveying the sites for possible hydro-electric stations, planned primarily for pulp and paper operations, and it appeared that this situation would soon be resolved.

If drilling continued to show favourable results, a large-scale base metal mine could be established. Probably as much as $20 or $30 million was needed and there was much speculation as to how the Mattagami Syndicate would raise the necessary capital. These questions were answered in May, 1958, when it was announced that Noranda Mines, McIntyre Porcupine Mines, and Canadian Exploration Limited would share equally in financing further development and production, under the direction of Noranda. The Mattagami Syndicate turned the property over to the Noranda group under a working option agreement which stipulated that 80,000 additional feet of diamond drilling, costing $400,000, would be completed by December 1, 1959, during which time the members of the syndicate would be able to exercise their option to form a new company. Thus, Mattagami Lake Mines Limited was incorporated under a Quebec charter in 1958, capitalized at six million shares, two million of which were issued to the six members of the syndicate as vendors.

As Noranda began operations on the site, Dome and its partners were exploring nearby claims, and Watson Lake Mines Limited was incorporated to examine 80 claims two miles from the original orebody. The six companies in the syndicate also shared in two other ventures which made news at the time. The first of these, the Kitchigama Syndicate, explored extensive holdings in the vicinity of Grasset Lake, west of Mattagami Lake, and the second, the Kesagami Syndicate, involved exploration of 1,400 claims straddling the interprovincial border near the Turgeon River. The Kesagami operation was carried out with the greatest possible secrecy and, in an elaborate effort to conceal activities, field crews were flown from Cochrane, Ontario, 100 miles away.

At Mattagami Lake Mines, shaft sinking to 1,184 feet had been completed and lateral development was underway in 1959. By the end of 1971, reserves were reported as 15,893,160 tons averaging 8.8 per cent zinc, 0.66 per cent copper, 0.012 ounces gold and 1.08 ounces silver per ton.

The mine was put into production in October, 1963, at a daily rate of 3,000 tons, shipping zinc concentrates to the new Valleyfield, Quebec, plant of Canadian Electrolytic Zinc, to Quebec City for overseas export and to the United States. Copper concentrates were shipped to the Noranda smelter at Noranda, Quebec.

Over the years, the Mattagami Lake operation proved very profitable for Dome. In 1979 it was merged with Noranda Mines, with Dome receiving shares of Noranda in exchange for its Mattagami shares.

Dome, in 1958, held 18.4 per cent of the outstanding shares of Dome Petroleum Limited. "The past year," Michel said of the oil side of Dome's operations, "was a satisfactory one." Although there had been a drop in the demand for Canadian oil, Dome Petroleum was successful in increasing production by 16 per cent to 1,100,000 barrels. The Dome Mines affiliate held two million net acres in the western provinces, the Northwest Territories and Ontario, and also had interests in two gas and liquified petroleum gas producers. Dome Petroleum appeared to be off to a good start in the increasingly exciting field of "black gold."

The fifties ended with a celebration of the golden anniversary of Dome Mines and the staking of the first claims in the Porcupine camp. To mark the occasion, special jubilee events were held in Whitney Township, South Porcupine and Timmins, which included Firemen's Races, a Soap Box Derby, and a Regatta held on Porcupine Lake. The Whiskereeno Contest was also guaranteed to attract both participants and onlookers, with prizes being given for the best examples of the following types of beards: Heaviest, Lady Killer, Upsweep, Chin Whisker, Edward VII, Goatee, Lamb Chops and Scruffiest. The three-day gala was capped by an "R.C.A.F. Jet Fly-Over and Round and Square Dancing at the Edgewater Pavilion."

President Michel pointed out that the mines of the Porcupine camp, having produced bullion valued at more than $1.25 billion, had become "the greatest gold mining camp in the western hemisphere." From the start of production in 1910 to 1958, Dome Mines milled 23,474,714 tons of ore and extracted 7,234,292 ounces of gold and 1,195,641 ounces of silver, with a combined value of $219,462,598. Its first dividends were paid in October, 1915, and have been paid quarterly, without interruption, except for a brief period during the First

World War.

As the decade ended, Clifford Michel moved from the presidency to become Chairman of the Board and was succeeded as President by Redpath. As the dual leadership settled into place, they set their sights on a new venture in western Canada, which later became Canada Tungsten Mining Corporation Limited.

CHAPTER 16

"Granddaddy goes Grandly on"

After half a century, the Company was, *The Northern Miner* proclaimed, "bidding fair to become the all-time 'granddaddy' of Canadian gold mines." The Big Dome was "getting its second wind when most of its contemporaries, if they have not already expired, see the handwriting on the wall . . . (Dome) is giving every sign that it will outlive all the other producers of this famous camp." The newspaper also commended management for "its (consistent) ability to keep costs at the lowest possible level." It continued:

> . . . The orebodies are widely spaced, but the Dome property is a big one; it straddles the favourable zone for a length of 3-½ miles. The fact that the ore deposits are scattered over a big area means that a great deal of lateral development must be done. On the other hand, the progression to depth has been relatively slow, and Dome must surely hold something of a record that it has been able to exist without deepening its shaft. The sinking of the new internal shaft (to 4,860 feet), which just got underway a few weeks ago, represents the first shaft sinking to be done in 22 years.

Over the next few years, Dome was severely affected by labour shortages resulting from the opening of the new Texasgulf mine (later renamed Kidd Creek), in nearby Kidd Township, with its particularly rich copper-zinc-silver orebody. The new mine attracted many skilled hands from the district with its high wages, comparable to other base metal mines across the country. Due to the limited life that is characteristic of mines, there are many mine workers who come and go according to the fortunes of the mines. Dome, however, was able to retain a core of loyal employees who managed to keep the mine operating during this period.

In addition to this shortage of skilled labour, the mine also experienced uneven tonnages during the early sixties. Ore grade and reserves, however, were maintained through a systematic programme of drilling and underground exploration, resulting in the discovery of new ore. Before the end of 1963, the new internal shaft, No. 7, had been sunk to provide six new levels. The 34th level, at 4,628 feet, was opened first as there was evidence of a continuation to depth of two ore-bearing structures. One of these was a typical ankerite vein of above-average grade.

A stroke of good luck befell Dome during the reconstruction of the "back road" to Timmins, which cut across the Dome property. A quartz vein was uncovered between the main shaft and the former Dome Extension property, and a few hundred tons of good grade material was removed by a power shovel, providing the mill with a "sweetener."

During these early years of the sixties, Dome began to benefit from technological improvements adopted to reduce costs and increase efficiency. In the summer of 1960, coal-fired boilers were replaced with natural gas units, and the next year a modern crushing plant and a conveying system were purchased from a recently closed uranium mine. Other operational improvements included increased mechanization of the timber yard and changes in both the water supply system and the disposal of tailings. A significant saving was realized in 1961 with the conversion from dry pit sand, which had to be hauled five miles to the mine, to classified mill tailings for hydraulic backfill underground. This resulted in an overall saving of $1.32 per ton of backfill in place. "All of these (modifications)," said Girdwood, "are worthwhile whenever a quick return, in improved operating costs, can be seen for a modest capital expenditure. That, of course, is not new — it's just plain good business."

C.C. Calvin, associated with Dome since 1923, died on August 3, 1963. Calvin was an important link to the early days of Dome, having served as Secretary and in later years as Vice-President. The Dome connection with the firm of Fasken & Calvin continued, however, as Bryce R. MacKenzie, a senior member of the law firm and Assistant Secretary since 1952, became Secretary and Director, and Girdwood assumed additional responsibilities as Vice-President.

The squeeze of low gold prices and spiralling costs of production continued to plague the industry. In 1958, Redpath commented on the EGMA Act in an address at a conference of provincial ministers of mines at St. Andrews, New Brunswick:

> . . . There is a very general understanding of the fact that gold mining is unique in that its product, gold, is a monetary metal, maintained at a fixed price by international agreement and thereby removed from ordinary laws of supply and demand and price variations in accordance with costs of production. We know of no other commodity to which similar conditions

apply. This fact, and the circumstances surrounding the production of gold, have resulted in the growth of important communities where tens of thousands of Canadians earn their livelihood and have a financial stake, make special treatment inevitable. Governments in Canada for the past 10 years are to be highly commended for recognizing, in the face of some skeptical but misguided opinion, that in its gold mining industry this country has a well established asset which it cannot afford to lose.

Dome management expected a revaluation of the price of gold in the near future, but six years later the situation had still not improved. As Chairman of Canada's oldest continuing gold producer and an authority on international banking, Cliff Michel commented:

> . . . The startling disclosures of profound inherent weaknesses in the (British) pound have prompted a large number of people to revive their interest in gold, almost of a sudden. There can be no doubt that the monetary conditions of this country along with uneasiness over the outlook for business in the coming year — especially as to inflation of production costs — are urging people to look again to gold as the traditional protection during troubled times as well as its own attributes.

Dome, however, did not stand idly by while governments discussed the future price of gold. Its exploratory arm took part in a joint venture, known as the Mackenzie Syndicate, which was launched in the late fifties by Karl Springer and J.M.R. Corbet, both of whom had initiated the Mattagami Syndicate. Other partners in this new venture included Leitch Gold, Area Mines, Highland-Bell, and Ventures (now Falconbridge Nickel Mines).

For many years there had been rumours of gold finds near the Nahanni River and its tributaries in the Northwest Territories. Late one year, two trapper-prospectors appeared at Fort Nelson with gold nuggets reportedly coming from this area. While heading back to their find the next spring, however, they and their secret drowned. There had also been some evidence of scheelite (tungsten mineral) in the same region. Acting on this, the Mackenzie Syndicate sent their prospectors to the area equipped with ultraviolet lights to identify this mineral by fluorescence. This approach proved successful, for in November, 1959, Springer proudly announced that the syndicate had made a major discovery of tungsten in the Mackenzie Mountains. He was exultant: "It's a mine — in fact, it's probably the largest and richest tungsten deposit on this continent, if not in the free world!"

Tungsten had originally been used primarily in the manufacture of filaments for light bulbs and in tungsten-carbide tipped drills used by the mining and petroleum industries. It became increasingly valuable in the making of single point tools, milling cutters, wear-resistant parts, gauges and valve seats, the leading edges of snowplow and bulldozer blades, automobile tire studs, knives and computer parts.

Canada Tungsten Mining Corporation Limited was incorporated in 1959 to develop the rich deposits. Karl Springer, its first President, had, by March, 1961, arranged development financing. Initially, the five partners in the Mackenzie Syndicate each held 14.52 per cent of the issued capital, and Lake Expanse Mines held a 4.85 per cent interest. Later, Dome Mines, Ventures and Northwest Amax Limited, a subsidiary of American Metal Climax, agreed to buy a total of 1,500,000 shares at $1.10 and additional shares by December 31, 1963. They also agreed to purchase 6 per cent debentures of Canada Tungsten with a face value of $2,680,000, and to put up $1 million in working capital. The other shareholders in the Mackenzie Syndicate assented to the sale of shares to Northwest Amax in order to increase its percentage interest.

As the property was remote, development costs were high. Heavy machinery, equipment, tools, fuel, supplies and food had to be shipped from Vancouver, hundreds of miles to the south. Nevertheless, these enormous costs were worthwhile, as tests had shown that the property could produce scheelite concentrate of high quality which was readily marketable in Europe and in the United States.

Light bush planes were used to reach the property quickly and, as the area was mountainous (averaging 7,000 feet), this involved some hair-raising dodging and weaving between the unforgiving rocky slopes. One other common hazard was the presence of bears. When the Mackenzie Syndicate was close to completing preliminary diamond drilling at the site and the cold chill of winter could be felt in the air, a plane was flown in with spare parts needed for the drills and was parked on a makeshift airstrip a short distance from the cabins. The next morning, the astounded pilot gazed upon the remains of his ruined bush plane. Apparently, a bear (probably a grizzly that had been seen around the camp) had smelled the emergency rations inside and decided to open up the plane, which it did with a few swipes of its powerful paws just as easily as if it were opening a tin of beans. The only salvageable parts were the instruments; the fuselage, panels and other parts of the plane were more or less shredded. The insurance adjuster handling the case was forced to admit that this was the first time he had processed an airplane claim for "bear damage"!

The federal government, already building a development road in the area, paid two-thirds of the cost of a branch road to the tungsten property. In 1962, before spring break-up, 3,450 tons of freight had been moved in on a 75-mile

Pouring a bar of gold. (above)
Bars of gold bullion. (below)

temporary winter road and 700 tons had been flown in to a hastily constructed airstrip. By the end of that year, the plant was ready for business, complete with townsite, two-room schoolhouse and a curling rink. Meanwhile, preparations for mining had pressed onwards and by December, 92,000 tons of ore had been mined in the open pit and stockpiled at the site of the mill.

After this surge of activity and just as the mine became fully operational, the price of tungsten dropped drastically as a result of unexpectedly heavy world sales by China. At the time Canada Tungsten was financed, tungsten concentrate was selling at $18 a short ton unit (20 pounds) but by the spring of 1963 the price had plunged to $8. The Company, Springer insisted, "would be fully competitive in a normal commercial market," but conditions were not normal. The danger of possible releases of stockpiled tungsten in the United States and government-subsidized tungsten from South Korea and other countries further depressed the price. As a result, the Directors of Canada Tungsten were forced to cease production to await better times. Disposal of the concentrate on hand provided funds for property maintenance, so that the mine could be restarted quickly if and when economic conditions improved.

Luckily, it was not too long before this occurred. In 1964, the Company signed contracts for the bulk of its production, intending to sell the remainder on the open market at a higher price. Mining began in June and four months later the mill was back in full operation. By the end of 1965, the world price had risen dramatically to $35.50, and even though Canada Tungsten's contracts were signed at the lower 1964 prices, the Company showed a profit of $827,290 in 1966, its first full year of operation.

Then, just as the future was looking brighter and as the employees were on their way home for a Christmas break, fire broke out in the concentrator drying section. Four hours later the concentrator and the crusher were completely destroyed. Rebuilding began quickly and by November, 1967, a new fireproof mill was in operation. The leaching plant was also moved to North Vancouver to save the high cost of transporting process acid to the mine site. In 1980, Canada Tungsten was capable of producing 8 million pounds of tungsten a year, making it the largest producer of tungsten in the western world.

Dome gradually increased its shareholding to slightly over 20 per cent. Redpath, after retiring as President of Dome, accepted the chairmanship of Canada Tungsten, a position he still held in 1982. Malcolm Taschereau, his successor at Dome, also serves as a Director.

As the sixties drew to a close, Dome Mines celebrated the pouring of gold bar No. 10,000 at the Big Dome, 58 years after its beginnings in 1910. Walter Honer, Chief Assayer and Refiner of the Company, was given the honour of pouring the molten metal, a fitting tribute to his 49 years of service with the

Crown vetch, trefoil, Kentucky blue and other grasses planted by Dome to protect the abandoned tailings dams from erosion. (right)

The flower gardens at Campbell. The short growing season in northern Ontario is offset by longer hours of sunshine. (below)

Company. Since 1910, Dome produced gold valued at a phenomenal $280 million and paid out $110 million in wages and $93 million in dividends. In 1969, the Company's diamond anniversary, Dome had 950 employees, 18 per cent of whom had been on the payroll over 20 years and 34 per cent for ten years or more.

In 1970, Bryce R. MacKenzie, associated with Dome since 1952, resigned as a Director and Secretary because of failing health. He was replaced by Fraser M. Fell, formerly the Assistant Secretary.

Since commencement of milling operations in 1912, approximately 30.7 million tons of tailings have been deposited on surface and impounded in four dams covering 321 acres of land. In 1971, a programme of reclamation of these areas was commenced, employing a variety of seeding techniques, including crown vetch, trefoil, Kentucky blue and other grasses, shrubs and trees, to stabilize the abandoned tailings dams from erosion. The areas include not only tailings but also land that Nature left barren. By the end of 1981, 174 acres had been reclaimed and their appearance has added much to the aesthetic value of the surrounding area.

Early in 1971, Dome opened a field office in Timmins, "an excellent exploration and research base," according to Redpath. A slightly decreased budget for exploration was also explained: "The reduction in expenditures on mineral exploration does not signify any lessening of effort but rather a change due to a cycle of geophysics and preliminary investigation of a number of properties instead of the heavy expenditures on diamond drilling and underground exploration undertaken in 1970."

The search for copper in the 7,519-acre property of Clinton Copper Mines in Clinton and Marston Townships of Quebec provides an example of the kind of co-operative effort that interested Dome. This property, explored intermittently since 1959, was seriously investigated after Clinton Copper Mines' incorporation in 1963. The company was controlled jointly by Dome Mines and the Sullivan Mining Group, each holding a 35 per cent interest, with three other companies making up the remaining 30 per cent.

In 1970, a diamond drilling programme indicated reserves totalling 1,598,500 tons with a grade of 1.92 per cent copper, 1.36 per cent zinc, and low values of lead, gold and silver. At a time when the price of copper had reached an historic high, production began from one easily accessible and higher than average grade orebody, the ore being transported 35 miles by truck to a concentrator owned by Sullivan at Stratford, Quebec. By the end of 1972, however, the price of copper dropped to below 50 cents a pound and the project operated at a loss, continuing only a few months longer on a salvage basis. The "O" orebody was mined out to the surface and the decision was then made to close the mine. After final clean-up and sale of equipment, Dome incurred a small loss on the project.

The importance Dome management attached to exploration during this period was emphasized by the appointment of G.S. Wallace Bruce as Vice-President (Exploration). Since the death of James McCrea in 1953, all activities had been headed by senior geologists, with Dr. Paul Richardson, and later Bruce, reporting directly to Redpath.

By the early seventies, Dome's position as a leader of the gold producers in Canada was securely established, due mainly to the historic events that had occurred in the marketplace over the previous four years. In March, 1968, the world market price of gold began to rise steadily, reflecting more accurately its true value as a medium of exchange. Michel and Redpath explained the economic forces behind gold's rise in price that first year:

> Currency crises and devaluations, with implied upward changes in the price of gold, have been recurring phenomena of the post-war period. The year 1968 saw another one, which culminated in March in the inevitable end of the "gold pool," the artificial device whereby the United States and six other countries had attempted for a number of years to prevent the free market price of gold from rising above the official U.S. price of $35 per ounce. As the United States supplied more than half the gold offered by the pool in its stabilization efforts, it became obvious that to continue this policy during a decade when the U.S. was running a Balance of Payments Deficit would produce a drain on its gold reserves which, if carried on indefinitely, could result in their complete depletion. When it became apparent that such a condition would result in utter chaos to the international monetary system, the "pool" device was abandoned and the gold market in London and elsewhere was set free, with the price to be determined by the forces of supply and demand. This has become known as the "two-tier" gold price system, and since March, 1968, the free market price has fluctuated in a range of 10 per cent to 20 per cent above the U.S. Treasury price, with it currently (February, 1969) at the upper end of the range at $42 per ounce . . . It would seem to be evident that gold remains a keystone in the arch of any international monetary system . . .

After one full year of the "two-tier" system, the free market price of gold peaked at $43.82-½ (U.S.), dropping temporarily below the $35 official figure the next year, as private holders liquidated large amounts acquired from central bank reserves, primarily those of the United States, during the 1968 gold crisis. In 1970, Michel and Redpath reported:

> From a low of $35 per ounce early in the past year, free market prices moved up to over $39 in October and closed the year at $37.33. The upward trend we anticipate will certainly be an erratic one, but, in the inflationary environment that exists throughout the world, the free market price is likely to remain above the official price. Equally important in weighing this trend is the fact that official stocks of gold in the International Monetary Fund and central banks have increased by almost $1 billion since the introduction in 1968 of the "two-tier" system, indicating that the large industrial nations do consider gold an essential part of their ultimate reserve assets.

Dome shareholders were told the next year:

> The year 1971 was eventful for gold. In the free market its price trended upward from the $37-$38 per ounce range early in the year to nearly $44 in mid-August when the United States closed its "gold window" . . . U.S. gold reserves had fallen below $10 billion and official foreign central bank holdings of U.S. dollar claims had grown to several times that figure . . . By suspending the convertibility of these official dollar claims into gold at $35 per ounce the United States in effect had devalued its dollar against the stronger currencies of the free world. These currencies were then permitted to "float" upward, away from the exchange rates fixed under the International Monetary Fund agreement . . . As the U.S. has not yet increased the official price, it has created an uncertainty, during which time the free price of gold has been as high as $49.75 per ounce . . . Even though the U.S. attempts to demonetize gold, the rest of the major free countries of the world now hold more than twice as much gold as the U.S. and seem not prepared to accept a monetary system that does not have gold at some fixed price as the measuring rod of other currencies.

In 1972 the U.S. Congress established a new official price for gold of $38 per ounce, but did not restore the convertibility of the American dollar. Because of strong private demand, the price in London rose rapidly, hovering around the $65 mark late in the year. It was also in this year that Dome began selling its gold on the free market, disqualifying it for EGMA benefits, but resulting in a significant increase in revenue. The average price realized on sales during the year was $58.06 (Can.) per ounce in contrast to total revenue per ounce in 1971 of $45.03, including $9.70 per ounce under the EGMA Act.

At the mine, the mill had been forced to operate at 11 per cent below capacity, averaging 1,774 tons per day in 1972 due to a 7.2 per cent drop in labour. Girdwood commented: "This labour shortage has forced the closure of many narrow, high cost, and low production stopes in favour of wider, lower-grade and high production stopes where, in many instances, mechanization is applicable and efficiency higher." Although increased mechanization was implemented underground wherever possible, the use of this equipment to mine the narrower veins in the old part of the mine was limited. In mid-1972, the Company launched a temporary plan to attract the men it needed — a bonus of two cents an hour for each $1 the price of gold rose over $50, to a maximum of $70. This plan was officially discontinued in 1974, but the amount was incorporated into wages.

On October 1, 1972, Charles P. Girdwood retired as General Manager but remained a Vice-President, devoting considerable time to Company affairs. At South Porcupine, Harry V. Pyke was appointed Manager, with Robert J. Perry, who had been Mine Superintendent, becoming General Superintendent.

Pyke, born in Leicester, England, was a small child when he came to Canada with his family. For eleven years Pyke's father worked as a diamond driller at Dome and it was natural that Pyke should look to the mine for a summer job when he was in high school. When he was seventeen, he worked on what was called the "kid bull gang," young fellows who did odd jobs at the mine. In 1939 he got a job underground, for 58 cents an hour, as a "nipper," who had to recover the forged steel drill after a hole had been drilled and have it reforged. (This was before tungsten carbide drills came into use, and constant reforging was necessary.)

In 1941 Pyke left Dome to join the Royal Canadian Air Force. When the Second World War ended, he returned to Canada and enrolled in mining at Queen's University. Upon graduation in 1950, he returned to Dome and soon became a stope boss and later a shift boss. In December of that year, he left to work for Broulan Reef, a gold mine located a few miles northeast. Over the next 18 years he worked at a number of mines in Ontario and Quebec, occasionally returning to South Porcupine to visit friends and relatives. During one such stay he spoke with Charles Girdwood, a good business friend. It was not long until Dome's General Manager offered Pyke the position of Special Projects Engineer, which he accepted, and a year and a half later he was promoted to the position of General Superintendent.

Early in 1973, Michel and Redpath assured shareholders that they would take full advantage of high gold prices:

Management's policy will continue to be as low cost an operation as possible with the ore reserves it has developed and to use the new levels of gold prices to attempt to extend the life of our mines with mill feed that heretofore was not commercial at the artificially low official price that prevailed for so many years.

Later that year, world events, in particular the Israeli war and the escalation of crude oil prices, began to have an influence on the fortunes of business in the western nations:

It is obvious that the free market price of gold and the world market price of oil and gas established by the mid-eastern producers impact heavily on our Company's present and future earning power . . . In this atmosphere the price of gold, which had opened the year at the $64 per ounce level, rose rapidly in June to over $126 per ounce. Concurrently, the Arab world, noting that the dollars it was receiving for oil had less buying power, and sensing that the balance of power in the supply of oil had passed to them, took the occasion to triple the price of crude oil. These events, plus the Israeli war, touched off a second stage of the rise in the price of gold and it moved up from a level of $112 per ounce at the end of 1973 to approximately $169 per ounce, where it is at the time of this writing (February, 1974). If the Arab policy of escalation of crude oil pricing is not modified, there will be a readjustment of such magnitude in the holdings of the world's monetary reserves in their favour to the detriment of Europe, Japan, and the United States, as to make any forecast about orderly international monetary relationships and hence the price of gold all but impossible.

Michel and Redpath noted that the American dollar had been devalued twice within two years and in 1973 had been allowed to float freely against all other currencies. When the float continued downward "it created a crisis of confidence in paper currencies and it appeared to many that gold was once again the ultimate store of value."

The future appeared bright for Dome, despite an economic situation which perplexed even the experts. *Forbes*, the American business magazine, interviewed Michel in the late summer of 1973. The 62-year-old Chairman, who glowed with "the smug serenity these days that comes of seeing 30 years of patient effort at last rewarded," told the interviewer, "The last thing I ever expected was that, after struggling since 1944 to hold this old gold property together until the gold price went up, we'd see the price of oil and gas going up at the same time."

Michel hoped Dome would double its earnings in 1973, but this proved to be an underestimation. Consolidated net income was $7.56 a share, as compared to $3.74 of the previous year — "the highest the Company has recorded since operations began in 1911." This record-breaking income included, of course, "improved earnings" from the 21 per cent equity held in the increasingly successful Dome Petroleum Limited.

The Chairman pointed out that the rise in the price of gold also brought other benefits to Dome Mines. Lower grade ores, now economic to mine, resulted in slowing the decline in Dome reserves which had taken place over the years. "We have been telling our shareholders for years that its (the mine's) life was limited," Michel said, "but at $60 an ounce it will live at least another 10 years ... The ounces you produce per ton may go down, but if you're getting $100 an ounce instead of $40, your revenues are going to go up."

Michel emphasized that his real thrust would be the increased expenditure of some $1.5 million a year on exploration and the building up of treasury reserves, should "something big" turn up.

By 1974, the Dome group of companies — Dome Mines, Campbell Red Lake and Sigma Mines (Quebec) — was Canada's leading gold producer "by a country mile," as *The Northern Miner* put it. Although naturally proud of its good showing, management was less than exuberant. "We have had a good year," President Redpath said, "but we have had to wait 20 years for this." The higher gold prices enabled Dome to offset "sharply higher operating costs due to continuing and escalating inflation, in addition to unprecedented increases in rates of taxation." The effective combined income and mining tax rate on operating income increased rapidly from 38.4 per cent in 1973 to 56.2 per cent in 1979, exceeding the tax rate levied on all other industries.

At the beginning of 1974, gold was being sold at $117 (U.S.) an ounce, jumping to $180 in three months and then dropping to $129 by July. The Dome report commented:

> At this point, the United States government began to indicate a change in its policy that would permit its citizens to legally hold gold, beginning in 1975, causing a move to $195 per ounce during December, with the year's closing at $187 ... These gyrations in 1974 took place within a framework of unsettled confidence associated with an unparalleled world-wide price inflation on one hand and the beginning of a business recession on the other. Financial uncertainties existing during the year were interest rates at historic high levels, international balance of payments deficits related to the Arab oil cartel's pricing policies, and a continuing decline of the U.S. dollar exchange

rate against those of its major trading partners. It would appear that, at a time when the U.S. dollar weakens in a world where exchange rates are no longer fixed by "float," there is a tendency to destroy confidence in all paper currencies and stimulate the demand for gold.

It was only two years later that Clifford Michel died after a brief illness. Michel's successor as Chairman was A. Bruce Matthews, a Director of Dome Mines since 1947, who had a long and notable career in finance and senior business management that began in 1932 with Matthews and Company, the investment house founded by his father, the Hon. Albert Matthews, Lieutenant-Governor of Ontario from 1937 to 1946. Bruce Matthews brought to Dome experience gained as chairman of Excelsior Life Insurance and Canada Permanent Trust; as a member of the International Advisory Committee of Chase Manhattan Bank, N.A.; and as a director of many prominent companies, including Hollinger Mines, Massey-Ferguson, Domtar, Aetna Life and Casualty, Standard Broadcasting, and Dome Petroleum. He was also Executive Vice-President of Argus Corporation Limited during the presidency of the late J.A. (Bud) McDougald, and President following McDougald's death until his own retirement from Argus in 1979.

Matthews gave distinguished service to his country in the Second World War, beginning in 1928 when he joined the Canadian Militia as an artilleryman. He rose steadily through command ranks, as a brigadier in Italy and northwestern Europe, and finally as Major-General commanding the 2nd Canadian Division. He holds the honours of Commander of the Order of the British Empire, Grand Officer of the Order of Nassau, the Legion of Honour, and the Croix de Guerre with Palm. During combat service he was twice mentioned in dispatches.

After the death of Cliff Michel, his son, Clifford L. Michel, was appointed a Director. Known to his friends as Mickey, he is a partner in the prominent New York law firm of Cahill Gordon and Reindel. His appointment was more than a tribute to his father, as it was also an acknowledgement of his own legal and business expertise acquired in the United States and France. But the presence of the senior Michel, a good friend to many at Dome and highly respected throughout the business community, was sorely missed.

CHAPTER 17

Clifford W. Michel: "Financial Genius"

"As a man of great vision, wisdom, and integrity, he had few peers in the business of investment and finance, and he gave unstintingly of his time and talent to the promotion and development of the Company."

This was the praise voiced by Chairman A. Bruce Matthews and President James B. Redpath upon the death of Clifford W. Michel, who had been associated with Dome Mines Limited for 37 years.

"He was a financial genius and the Company really moved ahead in his time."

This view of Michel was held by Dr. William F. James, consulting geologist and another long-time business friend and fellow Director of Dome. Dr. James, like Matthews and Redpath, had watched Michel skillfully steer Dome through the treacherous financial waters of the mid-forties, continuing right through to the first half of the seventies.

Michel was born in Brooklyn, New York, on September 4, 1911. He was of French-American extraction, with his grandfather being born in France, his father, Clarence Michel, in the United States and his mother, Matilda E. Moore, to Irish and American parents.

An only child, Michel attended public school before enrolling in Columbia University. He graduated with a B.A. in 1930 and a Master of Commercial Science in 1931 from Dartmouth College and the Tuck School of Business Administration.

Although Michel was involved in so many financial ventures across North America, these activities did not hinder his energetic participation in community life. He was a warm and generous person, greatly concerned about people and their welfare, who always said: "The little man has to have his day. If a man does a good job he should be rewarded accordingly."

As a young man working in New York, he became a friend of the Bache family and was often a guest at their Wenonah summer camp. It seemed inevitable, then, that he and Barbara, the youngest of Jules Bache's granddaughters, would fall in love. Barbara, then only fourteen, told her family that she wanted to marry Clifford and was quickly packed off to Europe to cool the budding romance. Happily, however, in true romantic style, the couple became engaged in 1936, when Barbara had become a young lady of seventeen, and they were married the following February.

The Michels had three children, Clifford Lloyd, Julienne Moore and Barbara Ellen. They were a private and close family, with the parents often including the children in their vacation plans, especially during the summer holidays.

The Michels founded the Barbara and Clifford Michel Foundation, Inc., a charitable organization. Michel was also a trustee of St. Luke's Hospital and an active supporter of the Cancer Wing of the Columbia Presbyterian Hospital, both of New York City. Michel was a Senior Warden of St. James Episcopal Church and his wife was active on the church's committees.

The Michel fortune came from a fund of $4 million left by Jules Bache to his family. When Michel joined J.S. Bache & Co. in 1939, Bache appointed him to oversee this fund which was then kept in a holding company. Michel eventually built it up to $98 million, and at the time of his death it was worth about $80 million.

He became senior officer or director of several firms, including J.S. Bache and Company, Loeb Rhoades and Company, Tennessee Corporation, Miami Copper Company, Cities Service Company, Atlantica del Golfo Sugar Company, Toronto-Dominion Bank Agency, Association of Stock Exchange Firms and, in Canada, Dome Mines Limited, Dome Petroleum Limited, Sigma Mines (Quebec) Limited and Campbell Red Lake Mines Limited. In 1939 he was elected to the Board of Dome and, from that time on, the South Porcupine mine and everything connected with it absorbed his attention, even during the Second World War, when he served as a major with the U.S. Army.

In 1940, he became a Vice-President of Dome and two years later Treasurer, following in Bache's footsteps. When Bache became the first Chairman of Dome in 1943, Michel was elevated to the presidency, at the age of only 32, bringing with him the vigour of youth. Over the next four decades he would lead Dome through its most challenging and rewarding undertakings.

Michel told an interviewer for *Forbes* of his strategy: "Until then (when he had become President), the Directors had paid out virtually 100 per cent in dividends. What we did was gradually shrink the dividend back and try to build up a treasury." Michel's main reason for this was to be able to take advantage of golden opportunities when they presented themselves. A large treasury indeed was needed for Michel's first major venture, the creation of Dome Exploration (Western), which would allow participation in the oil business in Alberta. With the purchase of lands in the Redwater field and the backing of institutional investors, Michel led the way to what has now become Dome Petroleum Limited. His financial forethought allowed Dome to assist in the development of Campbell Red Lake and Canada Tungsten.

Although he held conservative attitudes towards business, Michel had great faith in Dome Mines. This was amply demonstrated in 1971, when the future of the South Porcupine operation looked bleak. Profits fell by 80 per cent from the previous year, with the last quarter showing an operating loss. The average price for gold at the time was $35.33 (U.S.), with an additional $9.70 per ounce received under the EGMA Act. General Manager Girdwood had recommended to the Board that the present policy of mining average grade ore be followed to extend the life of the property as long as possible. If the price of gold did not improve substantially, however, periods of lean profits could result. If the Board felt otherwise, though, it would be possible to reduce tonnage and raise the grade by mining only the best grade ores, resulting in increased profits for a period of three or four years, after which time the property would become uneconomic at present gold prices. Michel's reaction to this alternative was short and direct: "God forbid!" As Bryce MacKenzie recalled, "Michel expected better times — and how right he was!"

He took a keen interest in nearly all aspects of the Company's operation, even though its financial condition was his main concern. "He followed the course of every drill hole," said Edmund Andrecheck who, as Assistant Treasurer and then Treasurer, worked closely with Michel.

Clifford Michel possessed an intuitive grasp of the economics of gold. His quick intelligence and sound reasoning provided Dome with a solid and reliable foundation, silencing disquieting rumours and bolstering the sinking hearts of those in the industry when market conditions seemed shaky. Michel's own philosophy with regard to gold, and his faith in its future were reassuring through very difficult times. Whenever an objective, confident point of view was needed, his opinions were sought and widely respected.

The Board of Directors usually made an annual visit to the mine, generally on the first weekend following the American Thanksgiving Day late in November. At that time of the year, the Directors often had a taste of early northern Ontario winter which, of course, had set in long before the southerners had even thought of putting on their overcoats. On one such occasion, a winter storm coated their plane with snow and ice which had to be cleaned off using the best implements the pilot could find — curling brooms from the Dome Mines club.

Michel enjoyed these meetings immensely because they provided an opportunity to meet and talk with the engineers and geologists who worked on the site. The Directors always discussed the problems of the day with full respect for the views of their confrères, and looking back over thirty years of such meetings, Bruce Matthews cannot recall any discussions that might have been regarded as acrimonious – indeed, he cannot remember any really serious disputes. Naturally, there had been differences of opinion, but these were resolved without anger or divisions. Matthews, a former stockbroker, also recalls that Dome Mines had always stood out as one company which, even in the thirties, "never needed to peddle shares."

When Michel accepted the challenges of Dome's presidency, he was well aware of the somewhat unsavoury reputation the mining industry had acquired as a result of the machinations of a few unscrupulous individuals. He was, however, able to maintain Dome's high standing in the business throughout his regime.

He continued to be as active as ever until just a few months before his death at the age of 65 on March 8, 1976. During the funeral service for him in St. James Church, part of the prayer described his unique personality:

> . . . He loved his work and colleagues. Quick of mind, intuitive in spirit, he went directly to the heart of things — in finance and commerce as in personal relations and community affairs. Trusting, generous almost to a fault, he embarked upon life with enthusiasm, perception and an infinite sense of responsibility. He was one of those men who by his presence, honour and intelligence held things together.

The Michel era came to an end, and to other hands was entrusted the responsibility of managing Canada's most enduring gold producer. A. Bruce Matthews, a distinguished divisional commander in the Second World War and a financial manager identified with some of Canada's largest corporations, stepped in to take the helm.

CHAPTER 18

The Dome Family

Dome has successfully integrated various ethnic groups in its labour force, which has been a stabilizing influence of inestimable value to the Company's continued success. The distribution of this veritable "United Nations" of workers over the past 29 years is as follows:

Percentage of Labour Force
According to Ethnic Background

	1952	1981	25-Year Club 1981
Anglo-Saxon	43	45	55
French-Canadian	16	29	8
Central European	17	13	12
Italian	15	9	20
Scandinavian	9	3	4
Other	0	1	1
	100%	100%	100%

Many second- and third-generation employees are still at the mine, a loyal and conscientious family that has supported the Company through good and bad times. This has long been a striking feature of Dome Mines. About a quarter of a century ago, 27 per cent of the work force consisted of father-son combinations, and Dr. William Line, a psychologist at the University of Toronto, suggested three reasons why successive generations felt an attraction for Dome and why the Company had so many long-service employees:

1. Dome provides good working conditions, wages and related benefits, as well as steady employment.
2. Dome employees enjoy well-developed recreational facilities and community activities at or near the mine site. The site is also conveniently located for those who like to hunt or fish in the surrounding wilderness.

3. The numerous father-son combinations are examples of "occupational inheritance," whereby a son tends to follow the occupation of his father. This practice is fairly common in isolated communities, where there are limited opportunities for work unrelated to the dominant industry.

A good example of this type of company-family relationship is the ongoing service of the Millions family, which began when the mine opened and has continued, from one generation to the next, to this day. It started in 1911, when Percy Millions, a carpenter, travelled on foot by boat to look for work in the booming Porcupine camp. He was hired by Dome and continued working for the Company until his death in 1939. Percy's five sons also worked at Dome while their father was there: Percy Jr., who later moved on to Manitoba where he became involved in the summer resort business; William, a carpenter like his father, who left the Company in 1944 and returned ten years later; Stanley, a yardman, boilermaker and plate shop foreman; Robert, a driller; and Harold, acting mill superintendent, who retired in 1979 after half a century of service. Harold's sons — Norman, Merv and Robert — were also on Dome's payroll at various times.

From 1920 to 1925, several Cornishmen emigrated to Canada and thirty found immediate employment at Dome. One of them was Harry Libby, who went on the Dome payroll in 1924 and worked variously as a driller, deckman, cage-tender and trammer boss. His two sons, both electricians, were also employed at Dome, Basil for twenty years and Reginald for fourteen years. His wife, who loved her new life in Canada, wrote such glowing letters home about the family's adopted land, that her three sisters promptly emigrated to Canada and married Dome employees as well — Bentley Webb, Alfred Stanlake and John Beard. Beard was a hoistman whose two sons, John and Harold, worked with him, and whose daughter, Lynn, married another Dome employee, Lawrence McGinn. McGinn's father, John, was also a Dome man.

John McGinn and his brother, Andrew, grew up on a farm at Cobden, in the Ottawa Valley. John was the first to leave for greener pastures. He took a job at Dome in 1921, and was joined by Andrew three years later. Besides Lawrence, John McGinn and five other sons worked at the mine: James, John and Arnold, Dome hands for several years, and Alex and Stewart, who both learned the machinist's trade before moving to Vancouver. Andrew's son, Gordon, was a diesel mechanic at Dome.

There was something about Dome that attracted men to South Porcupine and induced many of them to spend all of their working lives there. They knew no better life and wanted no other and, as their employer was fair, gave their best in return. Jack Pecore was one such man. He started as a hoistman in 1930,

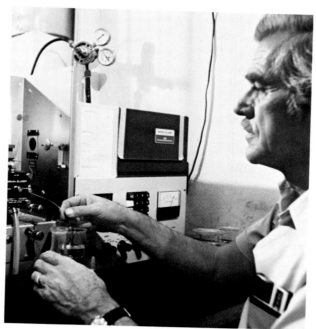

Dome chief assayer using atomic absorption apparatus for gold analysis. (right)

Preparation of solutions in Dome assay office. (below)

and after twenty-nine years, retired as a hoistman. During that lengthy service, he had carefully trained nearly one hundred younger men, one of them his son, Don, in this exacting job. Jack Pecore was proud of his position and gladly passed on his knowledge to others to make them, in due course, as skillful as he was.

The job of hoistman is one of the most important in a mine, as it involves the safe transport of as many as forty men in the lift cage when there is a shift change. He must be in good physical condition and pass an annual medical examination. He ensures that his cage is at least as safe as the elevator in any office building by "drop" testing the cage every three months and sending sections of the hoisting cables to the Ministry of Labour laboratory in Toronto for examination and testing at periodic intervals. There are safety "dogs" which stop the cage if there is any slackness in the "rope" (actually a steel cable), which must be inspected every day.

The hoistman alternates between cage hoists which carry men and skip hoists which move ore. In an eight-hour shift, a hoistman may raise up to 240 loaded skips, which travel at a rate of 1,600 feet a minute and move as much as 1,320 tons of ore. He must be alert, always aware of the signal bells that tell where the cage is to stop.

But not everyone can or would want to be a hoistman. A mine like Dome offers a fascinating assortment of jobs, where men and women may make use of their particular talents, or learn new trades. One man who found the career he wanted at Dome was Harry H. Costain, who studied minerals as a hobby and built up an extensive rock collection.

Costain came to Canada in 1907 from the Isle of Man, and in 1909 he and his father, John, started in business as stonemasons in Cochrane. Two years later, John left for Porcupine and was there when the devastating fire of 1911 broke out. During this time, Harry was with the crews fighting the flames that threatened Cochrane. When the fire was finally brought under control, Harry, worried about his father and unable to find out anything because the fire had destroyed communication lines between the two communities, made his way to Porcupine, where he found his father safe. He decided to stay in the mining camp, found employment with Dome and remained for forty-two years.

For many years Harry Costain was, appropriately, the fire warden at the mine and was also responsible for the painting of all mine buildings. In addition, time clocks were placed in his charge after they were first installed in 1924.

John Costain also found work at the Dome. At one time, three generations of Costains were on the payroll: John, Harry and Harry's two sons, Orry and George. Harry's daughter married Irwin Richardson, a Dome shift boss.

Because of his interest in minerals, Harry took a prospector's course offered by the Ontario Department of Mines in 1921. He began acquiring minerals of various sorts from the Porcupine area as well as other parts of Canada, the United States and, by purchasing and trading, from other countries. His collection of over 2,000 specimens has been exhibited in many parts of Canada and is now the special pride of the district. Harry Costain delighted in showing his collection to young geologists, as he would often prove them wrong on a number of specimen identifications. After his death, the collection was purchased by the Porcupine mines and is now displayed as the Costain Collection in the McIntyre Community building in Schumacher.

There are many employees from all ranks who have served the Company for twenty, thirty, forty years or more. Here are a few examples:

At the time of his death, Clifford Michel had been with Dome Mines for thirty-seven years.

James B. Redpath had been with the Company and its subsidiaries for forty-seven years, and was still active in Dome's affairs in 1982.

Charles P. Girdwood was with the Company from 1939 until his retirement in 1976, and continued to be called upon from time to time to serve Dome as a consultant.

Allan Pearce, a popular figure at the mine, retired in Canada's Centennial year after fifty-one years of service. When he started working with Dome, the mine had four mules hauling cars in the "Glory Hole" — a far cry from the complex operation of today. In later years, Pearce became well-known throughout the community as an artist, painting Dome's safety posters, and as an avid gardener. He also served as a mine surveyor and draftsman for many years, and his thorough knowledge of the mine made him an ideal guide for hundreds of visitors to Dome.

"Dead Eye" Jack Draper, a self-proclaimed "gun nut," worked at Dome for thirty-two years, starting in 1942. During these years he received international recognition for his marksmanship, having won the coveted silver medal from Bisley, the widely-known British shooting competition, in 1950.

Arthur D. Robinson had forty years of service at the time of his retirement as General Superintendent in 1971. Two other senior men at the mine recorded almost half a century of employment with Dome when they went on pension: Walter Honer, Chief Assayer and Refiner, forty-nine years upon retirement in 1969, and Frank Huggins, Chief Mine Engineer, forty-six years on retirement in 1979.

Frank Huggins and his three brothers arrived in Timmins during the depression years, when jobs were scarce. They agreed to stay six months, spending their time playing in the Northern Ontario Hockey Association League and, if no work could be found by that time, they would return to Toronto. But Frank found employment with Dome as a surveyor's helper for fifty-three cents an hour and eventually all four brothers became Dome employees with one of them, Lyn, becoming Ventilation Engineer.

Huggins spent most of his working life as a mine surveyor and engineer underground. Ambitious and anxious to get ahead, he read everything he could lay his hands on about mining and took correspondence courses with the support of the Company. Even when retired, he was persuaded to use his special knowledge of the mine when the Company embarked upon its expansion programme. He has maintained his zest for sports throughout the years, especially for hockey, the game to which he devoted much of his life. His family and friends are still proud of the skills he gave to the Newmarket team the year it won the Memorial Cup.

As to his long relationship with Dome, Huggins feels there are three reasons for its strength: a down-to-earth attitude on the part of management, its "open door" policy, and reasonable and non-dictatorial supervision.

Dome Mines attracts and holds many who find opportunities for rewarding and satisfying careers. One member of Dome's staff, in thirty years of employment with Dome, rose from an engineering job to a senior executive position, making notable contributions to the advancement of the Company, but dying before reaching his full potential. He was James G.L. McCrea. After graduating in Arts from St. Michael's College and the University of Toronto, McCrea served in the Canadian Air Force during the First World War. Afterwards, he earned a degree in Engineering at Queen's University, working during the summers in the mines of northern Ontario and as a geologist with the Ontario Department of Mines in the Red Lake district. In 1923 he joined Dome as a field engineer and remained with the Company for the next thirty years. The highlights of his career included the launching of Sigma and the acquisition and development of Campbell, as well as a large measure of responsibility for the entry of Dome into the burgeoning oil and gas industry.

Prior to the Second World War, mining in Canada was solely a provincial responsibility and industrial organizations were set up on a provincial basis as well. Thereafter, however, the industry's rapid growth and the federal government's entry into mining policy, partially as a result of war requirements, indicated a need for closer co-operation. McCrea played a major role in the formation of the Mining Association of Canada, serving as its first President from 1946 to 1949.

In 1953, a year after McCrea's death, his colleagues in the industry, represented by the Canadian Institute of Mining and Metallurgy, paid tribute to his memory by conferring the Selwyn G. Blaylock Medal upon him, "awarded posthumously in recognition of a life characterized by distinguished service to

Canada, through exceptional achievement in the development of mines and mineral resources."

A succession of honours bestowed upon Dome employees during the seventies attest to the stature of the organization in the mining industry. In 1972, Charles P. Girdwood, then Vice-President and General Manager, was presented with the Distinguished Service (Gold) Medal by the CIMM, "in recognition of his many years of outstanding service to the mining industry of Canada in general, and to the Porcupine mining area of the Province of Ontario in particular, where he has contributed significantly to the industry, the Institute, and the welfare of the community as a whole."

In 1976, the Institute awarded President James B. Redpath the Inco Limited (Platinum) Medal for his "broad and unselfish leadership in the Canadian mining industry, particularly in the successful development of Dome Mines to a leading Canadian mining company."

In 1977, Basil V. Davis, Plant Superintendent from 1950 to 1977, was presented with the Donald J. McParland Medal for his "long and successful operating experience with major electrical installations in Canada and abroad and for his active participation in professional and community affairs." (His father, J.J. Davis, was Mill Superintendent at Dome from 1936 to 1954.)

Such honours were conferred not only upon Dome employees, but their wives as well. Each year, the CIMM presents the Sancta Barbara Medal, named after the patron saint of miners, in recognition of the important role played by women in the social development of Canadian mining communities. In 1978, the silver medal was awarded to Irene Holmes, wife of Dr. T.C. Holmes, retired Chief Geologist, "in recognition of her active participation and organizing abilities that enabled her to promote many athletic events in the Porcupine area, her active work in the Auxiliary which led to her becoming the first woman to be elected to the Hospital Board, her many years of devoted service to her church as head of the CGIT, her knowledge of children that helped to be instrumental in forming what is known today as the South Porcupine Nursery School, and her ability to welcome newcomers in the area, while caring for her home and four sons."

A second Sancta Barbara Medal was awarded in 1980 to Dorothy "Queenie" McCrea, widow of James, "in recognition of her service to the mining communities of Val d'Or and Bourlamaque, Quebec, and her contributions in enhancing the lives of those with whom she has come in contact, both English and French speaking, and for the example she set as a wife, mother, and diligent worker caring for the welfare of others and improving the communities in which she has lived."

Jim McCrea and his wife exemplified the family spirit that permeates the

Dome companies and were eminently suited for a life together in mining. Queenie was the daughter of C.W. Dowsett, who had served Dome for many years. Born in South Africa, where the Dowsett family spent much of their time before and after C.W. Dowsett's service as Dome's General Superintendent, she moved to Canada with the family when she was ten years old. She first met Jim McCrea when she was seventeen, and he proposed to her when she was twenty-one but, as her father had been asked to return to Northern Rhodesia to act as a consultant, she declined his proposal, preferring to remain with her family rather than be all alone in Canada. A year later, McCrea turned up in Johannesburg and proposed again and this time he was successful. Queenie and Jim were married in Northern Rhodesia in 1929 and made their first home at Dome. They later moved to the Sigma mine.

Charles William Dowsett had a distinguished career as an engineer and metallurgist, and was frequently called upon to provide expert advice to mines in South Africa, Canada and the United States. At various times from 1915 until Dowsett's death in 1952, Dome was particularly fortunate to have his expertise in solving metallurgical problems, notably primary grinding in water and pre-aeration of the pulp prior to cyanidation to oxidize pyrrhotite and other refractory sulphides. Many of his recommendations and innovations are still in use in the milling circuits at Dome, Sigma and Campbell, and his blending and mixing formulae and colormetric gold tests are used in gold metallurgy around the world.

As a reward for his many important contributions to the metallurgy of South African ores he was approached by Britain's Prime Minister, the Rt. Honourable Stanley Baldwin, on the recommendation of the governor of Northern Rhodesia, to accept a knighthood, but Dowsett, a very modest and retiring man, politely declined this high honour. His son, Kenneth, followed in his father's footsteps as consulting metallurgist at Dome from 1955 until his retirement in 1973.

Another fascinating family relationship, and one that directly links the present operating management of the South Porcupine mine to the discovery of the Big Dome in 1909, is that of the "Clan Campbell," the descendants of John George and Ida May Campbell. John and Ida had six sons and three daughters. Their first daughter, Ida Maud, was the wife of Jack Wilson, chief discoverer of the Dome. Two other sons, Frank and Cliff, were members of Wilson's prospecting party, with Cliff and his cousin, George, also being two of the stakers of Campbell Red Lake. Their second daughter, Della Mae, married J.B. St. Paul, and the couple had one son and four daughters, one of whom, Doris, is the wife of Harry V. Pyke, present Manager of Dome's South Porcupine operation. Pyke's father was also employed by Dome as a diamond driller for eleven years between 1924 and 1939. In 1982, Mrs. J.B. St. Paul was the only living child of John and Ida May Campbell, although the late George Campbell's wife, Gene, was still living at Red Lake near the mine which her husband had helped make famous.

The public recognition accorded to Mrs. Holmes and Mrs. McCrea demonstrates that the efforts of these Dome ladies went a long way toward making these remote mining communities good places in which to work and raise families. As for actual employment within the Company, relatively few women were ever on the payroll (with one exception in 1919), the prevailing view being that mining was strictly men's work, an opinion which lasted well into the Second World War. This all-male tradition finally ended in 1941, when the scarcity of men compelled the Company to hire women to work in its offices. The general office staff for the past several years, however, has been predominantly female, with the senior positions of Purchasing Agent and Timekeeper directed by Margaret LeBlanc and Phyllis Laneville respectively. Today, work underground is still performed by men. In fact, until quite recently, it was considered bad luck to permit a woman to go below surface.

"Dome was unique among mining companies in its attitude to people," states Dr. James. "It was tolerant and considerate of human feelings." Edmund Andrecheck, who retired as Treasurer and as Vice-President in 1978, recalls that the cook at Campbell Red Lake filled his kitchen dining room with tropical flowers and plants that flourished in the warm, steamy air. Some companies might have objected to this intrusion of a hobby into a place of work, but not so at Campbell Red Lake where Danny the cook happily tended his kitchen garden without objections.

Dome instituted a five-day work week at the beginning of 1966 and also provided statutory holidays and vacation with pay long before such benefits were made obligatory by Ontario law. Management took a keen interest in ensuring that workers had proper recreational facilities and were housed as comfortably as possible. Housing for some foremen and other key employees was provided on the property, and in 1942, there were 130 of these houses, rented at modest rates. Company-owned dwellings still exist today — thirty on or near the mine site, and ninety on the Dome Extension property east of the main plant.

Two miles from the mine stands South Porcupine, a bustling town of 5,000 people, many of them Dome employees. The town had been founded on the south shore of Porcupine Lake for the building of retail stores and businesses, homes, schools, churches and places for recreation and amusement. In 1938, the Company provided funds for an indoor community skating rink, a building that contained a coffee shop and a public hall for dances, badminton and

*Part of the townsite on Dome
Extension property in 1975. (above)*

*No. 3 shaft and headframe in 1975,
with partially filled open pit and location
of the famed "golden sidewalk"
in the foreground. (below)*

meetings. At the mine property a curling rink, tennis courts, soccer, softball and recreation fields, and open air ice rinks were also provided.

The curling rink was in recent years completely renovated with assistance from the Government of Ontario, the City of Timmins and Wintario. A club was responsible for the upkeep of the building and its facilities, which are also made available to the community at large. It is, of course, in constant use throughout the winter and is particularly popular with Dome pensioners and other senior citizens who congregate every Thursday afternoon for some highly competitive games.

One of the Porcupine district's most popular games is hockey. Many young players went on to carve themselves highly successful careers in professional hockey, especially during the golden era of the Toronto Maple Leafs. To mention a few of the many famous ex-Porcupiners: Allan Stanley, who was recently inducted into the Hockey Hall of Fame; Les Costello, now an ordained priest back in Porcupine; Frank and Peter Mahovlich; Bill Barilko, who scored the winning goal in 1951 to win the Stanley Cup, and whose number (5) was retired after his tragic airplane accident; Dean and Eric Prentice; John and Ivan McClellan; Don Lever; Walter Tkaczuk; Gerry McNamara, now acting general manager of the Leafs; and the late John McFarland, former assistant general manager of the Leafs.

The sports spokesman for the area is generally acknowledged to be Victor Travis, a Dome employee who has been a weekly contributor to the Timmins *Daily Press* since April, 1976. He began his working life in the Dome warehouse in 1944, moving to the general office six years later, and now serves as Senior Office Clerk. His off-duty interest is sports of any kind, but he confesses that he is much more an observer than a participant. He has an encyclopedic knowledge of the athletic activities of South Porcupine, Timmins, Schumacher, Porcupine and any other part of the region where players may kick footballs, chase pucks or bat balls.

Travis' sports column began as "Flashback" and recalled the highlights of sports events in the Porcupine area of thirty to forty years ago. Its first appearance described the games played in the 1935-36 hockey season by the South Porcupine Porkies (made up almost entirely of Dome employees), and the Timmins Blackshirts. Much effort and research goes into the column, which is all done in Travis' spare time. For him, though, it's a labour of love.

Another very popular figure who became legendary in the Porcupine district was Carlo Cattarello, employed in the survey office at Dome for nineteen years. He was an outstanding coach of South Porcupine hockey teams when the area was a "hockey hotbed," as Travis put it. But Cattarello did more than tell others what to do — he showed them how by setting an excellent example. He played senior hockey for the South Porcupine Porkies; he played second base for the town's baseball team; and he pitched in the local softball league. He also competed in tennis tournaments with his son, Carlo Jr., and his daughter, Sandra.

Cattarello began his coaching career in his mid-teens, when he was asked to coach a team of local boys. Within a few years, he was recognized as "one of the main cogs in the Porcupine juvenile machine." In 1952, Travis said, Cattarello coached the Timmins Holman Pluggers to the All-Ontario crown, igniting the "Porcupine reign of terror" over other juvenile clubs in northern Ontario. For those who wondered at his success, Travis explained: "Carlo had a natural ability to recognize talent in young athletes, not only hockey players, but also those boys who were active in baseball, softball and tennis. Carlo converted Allan Stanley into a defenceman at a time when Stanley's ambition was to play as a centreman in the N.H.L."

When he was in his mid-fifties, Cattarello moved to Kapuskasing, a town of 12,000 which lies ninety miles northwest of Timmins, to become the director of recreation for the municipality. His name was kept before the people of Porcupine in a column he wrote regularly which detailed the sports activities in and around "Kap," which was published in the Timmins *Press*. Over the fourteen or so years he was in Kapuskasing, he never lost his affection for the town in which he had spent so much of his life and had so many friends. Upon retirement in 1980, he returned to South Porcupine and to the very house which held so many fond memories for him.

In November, 1973, Dome formed the Quarter Century Club for its employees and pensioners, with 183 charter members. In the past nine years 253 have been inducted into the Club. An annual banquet is held in South Porcupine, during which presentations of an engraved certificate and a gold watch are made to all new members. In 1982 there were 178 active members (including four women), 107 of whom attended the banquet.

Of the hundreds of Dome employees who went on pension, the great majority have remained in the Porcupine area, proof of the community's strong roots. Even in the case of the foreign-born, only very few have returned to their homeland. Typical are Domenic Santaguida and Giuseppe Gatto, two riggers with Dome. Santaguida stayed with Dome for more than thirty years until his retirement in 1966, and Gatto, with thirty-seven years of service, retired in 1968. Both are enjoying their golden years in South Porcupine, which admittedly experiences a much more severe climate than their native land.

Although mining has been perceived by the general public as an occupation in a somewhat dangerous and risky environment, in actual fact, statistics in Ontario of compensable accidents show that such industries as logging, lumbering, building construction, trucking, shipbuilding, stevedoring, steel erection and foundries have a much higher rate, and that mining compares favourably with such industries as pits and quarries, steel mills, metalworking, automobile manufacture, road construction and farming.

The insistence of the Company upon strict attention to safety precautions has resulted in very few serious injuries. Shift bosses meet with their crews once a month to go over safety measures and the entire organization follows the safety programme designed by the highly regarded Neill George, who was at one time a safety specialist at Inco. There has not been, nor will there ever be, any relaxation in this high standard. To paraphrase an old saying, eternal vigilance is the price of safety.

During 1980, public attention was drawn to the sudden increase in fatal accidents in the mining industry in Ontario and Quebec. Dome's record has compared favourably with the industry average and the Company continues to improve working conditions and practices at all its sites. As a result of determined efforts by all of its employees and the institution of a Safety Incentive Award Programme, Dome's frequency of compensable accidents was reduced significantly, from 37.3 per million man-hours worked in 1979 to 18.2 in 1980, a reduction of 51 per cent, and to 15.0 in 1981, a further drop of 17 per cent. The contributions of all concerned in this achievement testify once again to the continuing co-operation of the employees and management throughout the various sectors of the mine, typical of the "Dome family."

Experience at Dome has proven that those who take care of themselves and their tools, carry out their jobs with all due respect for the attendant hazards, carefully following the safety rules and regulations, do live long and healthy lives. One such man was Hilton Miller, who began working at Dome in 1928 and continued there until his retirement in 1976. His first job was in the electrical shop, where he began work at the age of fifteen. After the 1929 fire, he was posted to underground work and for more than twenty years he worked as a driller and was later put in charge of the drift school. His father, Henry, a venerable man ninety-three years of age, was living in Timmins at the time of Hilton's death in 1982. Retired from Dome since 1955, Henry was also an example of good health and spirit.

One who was deeply involved with the day-to-day health of the Dome employees was Dr. William Taylor who, although never employed by Dome, has been a good friend of the Company and its employees.

Not long after graduating from Queen's University, young Dr. Taylor developed a lung condition that forced him to rest in a sanitarium for a year. Upon recovery, he re-entered his profession, accepting an offer to join an older physician in a mining community in northwestern Ontario.

DOME'S MANAGERS
(clockwise from top left)

C.D. Kaeding, 1915–1920
H.P. DePencier, 1921–1934
Joseph H. Stovel, 1935–1944
Robert E. Dye, 1945–1952
Charles P. Girdwood, 1953–1971
Harry V. Pyke, 1972–

When silicosis, a lung disease caused by the inhalation of silicate or quartz dust, became a compensable condition under new Ontario legislation in 1926, every employee was required, by law, to have a chest x-ray examination upon being hired and annually thereafter. Silicosis is extremely difficult to diagnose because the symptoms can so easily be confused with those of other ailments. For example, a miner with shortness of breath may believe he is affected by silicosis, when his problem may actually be the result of obesity.

Dr. Taylor acted as physician for the Workmen's Compensation Board and organized a clinic and office in Timmins for the examination of mine employees. He made every effort to be accurate and fair in his findings, fair to the miner and to the mines of Ontario whose Workmen's Compensation Board assessments made the diagnostic service possible. For half a century, Dr. Taylor examined the mining men and women who worked at the Porcupine mines, many of whom became good friends, and he remembers Dome as being most co-operative. In fact, Dome was the only company that gave its workers time off with pay for their annual examinations and provided them with transportation to and from the clinic.

A testimonial to the great service he has given to Dome, and Porcupine in general, is to be found in the five tons of x-ray films he amassed over fifty years. To those close to medical science, Dr. William Taylor, CM, FRCP (C), FCCP, is one of the country's authorities on silicosis.

Dome management did not, however, restrict its interest only to the employees' clinical state of health. One of its employees was an explosives expert who could set off a chute-blast so skillfully that nothing more than a few feet from the blast would be disturbed. The powder man had one weakness — after every pay day he "tied one on" in a South Porcupine tavern and on Monday either failed to report for work, spending a day or two in jail, or showed up somewhat the worse for wear. Anxious to ensure that his services were available every working day, management regularly checked with the local police to see if he was in their hands. If he was, which was nearly always the case, a senior staff member would drive from his home at the mine site to the town and put up the bail to set the wayward powder man free. He was then taken home and placed in the care of his family, who would ensure that their errant wage-earner would be on the job, sober, Monday morning.

In 1979, Dome and its subsidiaries instituted a share ownership plan, whereby "shares were purchased and distributed to employees at no cost in an amount based on the length of service of each employee," according to Matthews and Taschereau. This plan "increased interest in the efficient operation and growth of the companies." In the fall of that same year, and again in 1981 and 1983 pension plans for all employees were adjusted in order to "improve significantly the benefits to both active and retired employees."

In an age when the computer often seems to take precedence over the individual, the spirit of a family relationship that has existed for so long is perpetuated and exemplified in the continuing tradition of the gift of a turkey to every married Dome employee at Christmas time, with single employees receiving other gifts. This is a happy, old-fashioned custom which began in 1911 and which the Company enjoys perpetuating, as it stands as a symbol of the strong belief in the value of a corporate family whose members are as proud of their Company as management is of them.

CHAPTER 19

Dome Moves into the Eighties

In spite of the freeing of the price of gold in the mid-seventies, Dome Mines faltered somewhat as it fought inflation and labour shortages. In response to the long period of depressed gold prices and the shortage of experienced miners, Dome had reluctantly allowed internal shaft No. 7 to flood from the bottom at 5,084 feet up to the 4,000-foot level to preserve the shaft's timbers, and concentrated the available manpower in more productive areas of the mine until better times returned.

These were not far away, but until then some difficult periods had to be endured. Late in 1975, the price of gold dropped significantly. Although the average for the year, $161.85 an ounce, was 4.6 per cent higher than that of 1974, operating expenditures had increased 18.5 per cent in the same period. A major addition to earnings — $1,300,000 — came from Mattagami Lake Mines which, in addition to its own mining income, had acquired a substantial interest in a zinc refinery at Valleyfield, Quebec, and a 60 per cent interest in Mattabi Mines in the Sturgeon Lake district of Ontario.

In 1976 the price of gold continued its decline and averaged $123.13 for the year. To maintain the viability of the operation during this period of low gold prices, cost-saving measures, including the temporary suspension of a large percentage of mine development, were introduced. By attrition and normal retirements, the labour force was reduced 28 per cent to 534 at the end of the year. The mine operating profit at South Porcupine decreased to $269,000 from $4,043,000 in the previous year.

The price of gold strengthened in 1977, as did the health of Dome Mines and its subsidiaries. Although gold production on a consolidated basis decreased by 16,508 ounces from the previous year, net income increased, thanks to bullion revenue which averaged $162.77 per ounce. These figures were encouraging to the operators of the pioneer Dome mine, whose demise had been predicted for threescore years, as low-grade ore that had previously been uneconomic could now be mined profitably. Said Harry Pyke, "There are

Aerial photo of the Dome South Porcupine plant. (August, 1982)

millions of tons of gold-bearing material here. Whether it's ore or not depends on the cost of recovery and the price of gold."

That price was unlikely to decrease substantially, according to Matthews and Redpath. "Looking to the future, it seems probable the problems of international liquidity and balance of payments, together with strong inflationary pressures and the consequent erosion of the value of paper currencies, will continue to enhance the value of gold as a protection against the ever-declining value of our savings."

Although gold was still its prime target, Dome Exploration crews were hunting for base metals and uranium as well. "The main thrust of this programme," shareholders were told, "remains centered in Canada, with particular emphasis placed in the areas where the existing mines are located. An increasing proportion of activity is, however, being directed to the United States, including Alaska." The group (Dome Mines, Campbell Red Lake, Sigma and Dome Petroleum) spent over $2 million on exploration in 1978, but Wallace Bruce, Vice-President of Exploration, reported that, while numerous properties were examined and several tested by diamond drilling, "no significant mineral discoveries were made."

Later that year, a field office was opened in Reno, Nevada. Operations in Nevada, Utah, Arizona and California were conducted by a new subsidiary, Dome Exploration (U.S.) Limited, with Edwin S. Rugg as Manager. The chief minerals sought were gold, silver, molybdenum, tungsten and uranium. Dome also participated with three other companies in the Cordex Syndicate to drill for uranium on the Nevada-Oregon border and evaluate properties in Nevada and Arizona.

On March 28, 1978, Dome and its subsidiaries purchased a 10.1 per cent interest in Denison Mines Limited, a major producer of uranium, at a cost of $31,500,000. This purchase (50 per cent by Dome Mines, 40 per cent by Campbell Red Lake, and 10 per cent by Sigma) resulted in $3,140,000 in Denison dividends by the end of the year. Matthews and Redpath commented, "The purchase of these shares of a large and profitable Canadian uranium producer serves to increase the exposure of Dome and its subsidiaries in the energy resource field and complements the investment in oil and gas represented by the ownership in Dome Petroleum and Panarctic Oils Ltd."

The previous year had seen Malcolm A. Taschereau succeed Jim Redpath as President. Taschereau was born in the heart of mining country, at Noranda, Quebec, in 1928. The spirit of mining was imbued in the Taschereau family, as Malcolm's father, Roger, had been Chief Mining Engineer for the Province of Quebec and in the years 1924-1927 was employed by Dome as an engineer.

Taschereau, a 1953 McGill graduate in mining engineering, spent a year with

Malcolm A. Taschereau, President and Chief Executive Officer.

A. Bruce Matthews, Chairman of the Board.

Falconbridge before joining Sigma in 1954 as an engineer. From there he went to Campbell Red Lake as a shift boss and rose to Chief Engineer, General Superintendent, and Assistant General Manager. In 1970, he returned to Sigma as General Manager; five years later he was promoted to the newly created position of Senior Vice-President of Dome. He was subsequently named Executive Vice-President and, in 1978, became President of Dome Mines and Chairman and President of Sigma and Campbell.

That year also saw the appointments of Henry Brehaut and Douglas Scharf to the head office managerial team. Brehaut, with a degree in mining engineering from Queen's University and a Master of Business Administration from the University of British Columbia, was named Vice-President, Operations. Scharf, a graduate in economics from York University and a Chartered Accountant, was appointed Controller.

Dome's 70th year of production in 1980 arrived with optimism, triggered by a record average price received for consolidated gold sales during the year of $721.82 (Can.) per ounce, record earnings, plans for expansion, and the development of a new and promising property near the Ontario-Quebec border.

To help offset a shortage of skilled labour, Dome successfully operated an on-the-job training programme with the help of the Ontario government for several years. However, in its latter stages, Harry Pyke realized that the programme had been "severely restricted by the shortage of suitable trainees." He added, though, that "improved efficiency of mining due to mechanization increased tonnage to a point where mill throughput reached capacity." Notwithstanding the shortage of skilled men, the Company, in 1979, was achieving more with fewer workers, largely because of the efficiencies brought about by new machines and technology. At the time of Dome's Golden Jubilee in 1959, the payroll listed 930 names, but twenty years later this had been reduced to 650.

An intriguing aspect of Dome's history is the fact that it is among the few remaining gold mines that continue to use the pennyweight system in recording gold values on their assay plans and records. A pennyweight (abbreviated as "dwt") is equivalent to 24 grains, 1.56 grams, or 1/20 of an ounce Troy. (Production records have always included ounces Troy, which is the universal standard weight for precious metals.) Prior to 1934, when the value of an ounce of gold was fixed at $20.67 (U.S.), Dome assay plans recorded values in dollars at $20.67 per ounce. When the price of gold began rising in 1934, a decision was made to show all assays in pennyweights, which is almost the equivalent of the previous $20.67 per ounce figure. (This decision has been particularly helpful to the operating staff in maintaining continuity of records and thousands of assay plans for the past seventy-two years.)

There were renewed expectations for the old mine at South Porcupine as Dome entered the eighties. Much of the low-grade ore was now worth mining, with the price of gold ranging in 1979 from $474 to $850 (U.S.) an ounce. Taschereau noted that in 1979 the price of gold, although subject to "wide swings," roughly paralleled the rise in the costs of production. Then, what he referred to as "a significant bench mark" was reached when the price exceeded $300 in the fall of 1979:

> Suddenly we were no longer simply adjusting mining grades to reflect the higher prices but, in addition, these higher prices indicated at least the potential of attractive investment in new or expanded plants. This has been reflected here and elsewhere in an increased number of announced construction projects and in greatly expanded efforts in gold exploration.

"It appears," the Chairman and the President told shareholders, "that, at present costs and at prices in excess of $450 Canadian, it is possible to mine at a profit virtually all material with gold values in excess of 0.05 ounces per ton." They predicted:

> At current price levels and, for that matter, at levels significantly lower, the mining of lower average grades of ore is indicated. This may be reflected in a reduced production level with a view to extending mine life or, if justified, in expanding tonnage at a lower average grade. The second option is currently being proceeded with at Dome Mines, where a proposed programme to increase tonnage by 50 per cent to 3,000 tons per day . . . was announced recently.

This stunning announcement made headlines in both the daily and business press. It was clear that Dome, while continuing its exploration for new properties, intended to revitalize the parent mine to take advantage of the world price for gold. Brehaut pointed out that "a significant proportion of the cost of the programme is related to the required replacement of outdated mill and plant facilities." By mid-1980, much of the work was already in progress, including detailed engineering for the new 5,400-foot No. 8 shaft, to be located near the eastern limits of the property. A plan for the eventual replacement of all existing mill facilities was also being prepared. A new grinding section would be started as soon as possible, as well as replacement of the water supply system and the building of a new shops and warehouse complex. All work was to be carried out over a four-year period. In addition, Campbell Red Lake and Sigma were being re-examined for their potential for higher tonnage.

While the engineers were engaged in their detailed planning at South Porcupine, Dome Exploration (Canada) Limited was conducting the most extensive

PLANT EXPANSION AT DOME

*Outside thickener
(150 ft diameter). (above)*

*Thickener rakes, catwalk
and drive mechanism. (below)*

PLANT EXPANSION AT DOME

Mill building extension steel, fine ore bins, one of three steel pachuca agitators, concrete water storage tanks and 27.6 K.V. substation being erected. (top)

Commencement of 20 degree decline for the conveyor gallery to the 200 ft. level of No. 8 shaft. The shaft headframe is in the background of picture. View looking east. (below left)

View looking west of concrete conveyor gallery where it breaks through surface overburden with No. 3 shaft headframe and crusher house in background. (below right)

PLANT EXPANSION AT DOME

Commencement of slip form for No. 8 shaft concrete headframe. Concrete collar of shaft in foreground. (top)

Final concrete pour with slip forms and staging in place. The 138 ft. headframe was completed in 6 days and 8 hours. No. 8 shaft will be sunk to an initial depth of 5,400 feet. (bottom left)

No. 8 shaft headframe, shafthouse and temporary sinking hoist-room. Main hoist-room wall foundations in foreground. (bottom right)

mineral exploration programme in its history. Expenditures increased 97 per cent to $5,908,000 in 1980. During the year, 2,211 claims were staked; more than 300 diamond drill holes totalling 171,000 feet were drilled, adding up to 60 per cent of the exploration costs; 4,000 line miles of airborne geophysical surveys and 930 miles of ground geophysics were carried out.

In 1980, Wallace Bruce, Vice-President Exploration, and Lorne Halladay, Chief Geologist, were responsible for thirty-two new starts, raising the number of active projects to seventy-nine including participation in joint ventures with outside interests. Emphasis still remained on gold, "the Dome Group's particular field of expertise," as Bruce noted, and about 92 per cent of the expenditures were in Canada, with the remainder in the United States. Projects in Ontario and Quebec accounted for 70 per cent of the total, with special attention given to areas near Dome's producing mines.

Of all the activities in which Dome was engaged in the final year of its seventh decade, none rivalled the Detour Lake project: the development by Dome and Campbell Red Lake Mines, with Amoco Canada Petroleum Company Ltd., of a promising gold property at Detour Lake, 125 miles northeast of Timmins and just 8 miles west of the Quebec border.

The project had its inception with the staking of 26 claims by Amoco in May, 1974. Diamond drilling began in October and the values found in the first three holes were so encouraging that 362 more claims were staked around the original block. After 157,000 feet had been drilled (87 per cent in the original anomaly), a major zone was identified which, at 1,800 feet below surface, was still open to depth, meaning that its limits had not yet been determined. In the fall of 1976, a comprehensive study of the property began, including underground work which consisted of 3,000 feet of development and 32,500 feet of diamond drilling. At that time reserves were estimated at 6.2 million tons, averaging 0.19 ounces of gold per ton. "It was obvious," said one report, "that a significant discovery has been made."

The report also stated, however, that the price of gold early in 1979 was such that "the economics of the project were in doubt." Amoco therefore invited Dome and Campbell Red Lake to acquire an interest in the project. In the joint venture agreement subsequently made, "Dome and Campbell each had the right to earn a 25 per cent interest (and) must each spend $5 million on exploration and development work on the claims . . . Campbell is operator of the work programme."

Work carried out at the property was "to develop an understanding of the nature of the gold occurrences . . . . In 1980, 10,000 feet of development work and 40,000 feet of diamond drilling are planned . . . Including engineering studies and support services, project costs for 1980 are estimated to be in the

*Trench exposing bedrock at
a gold property. (above)*

*Exploration diamond drilling
of a gold prospect.(below)*

order of $8 million."

On January 21, 1981, Campbell Red Lake announced "plans to proceed immediately with construction." Capital expenditures before the beginning of production, planned for late 1983, would be an estimated $143,222,000. During 1981, the first year of construction, $22,756,000 would be spent on site preparation, construction of a permanent camp and definition drilling of an open pit. All major buildings would be constructed the next year, with delivery and installation of equipment scheduled for 1983.

A 2,200 tons per day open pit operation would begin late in 1983 and run through until 1989. By 1987, the mill capacity would have increased to 4,400 tons a day and an underground mine would come "on stream," with the open pit being phased out. The construction force would number 450 in 1982, with the initial mine operating force totalling 270 and rising to 490 as underground work replaced open pit mining.

A major problem was that of access to the isolated property. At first, most of the supplies could only be shipped over a winter road from La Sarre in neighbouring Quebec. From January, 1980, until spring break-up, sufficient supplies were taken in over this road to support a year of continued operation. Discussions were held with the Government of Ontario to see if an all-weather road could be built to Detour Lake from Cochrane or Iroquois Falls. Dome also sought assurances that electric power would be available. By early 1981, agreement had been reached with the provincial government for the construction of a 94-mile road, with "firm support" that Ontario Hydro would supply the power required, with the power line to be built by Dome and Campbell.

Ore reserves, estimated at 30,506,300 tons grading 0.125 ounces per ton, were "more than adequate for a 20-year mine life, and the potential for additional tonnage is excellent." Taschereau told the press that "the economics look better as the tonnage goes up," and expressed his belief that, in time, there could even be a 6,600 or 7,700 tons daily milling operation.

Detour Lake could be one of the most cost-efficient gold producers in Canada. Stripping of the open pit site would not be costly as the overburden amounted to only 30 feet. The orebody, as defined to the end of 1980, was 3,000 feet long and up to 150 feet wide. This large mining width allowed the use of long blast-hole stoping and trackless mining, significantly reducing underground mining costs. Milling costs would be low due to the use of autogeneous grinding after eight-inch primary crushing. Employment of the carbon-in-pulp process, instead of conventional filtration and zinc precipitation, should result in more efficient gold recovery and cut down the amount of space and mill equipment needed, thereby further reducing capital costs.

Taschereau, in an address delivered in early 1981 to a Timmins business group, outlined the problems of costs and inflation as they affected new ventures, and Detour Lake in particular:

> There are operating underground mines currently treating ore grades lower than Detour's 0.125 ounces, but in plants largely paid for in previous years. As far as I know, this is the lowest planned grade for a new installation. Problems of the erratic nature of the distribution of tiny amounts of gold in the host rock have been compounded by the very low average grade. Whereas at Campbell Red Lake, a decision was made in 1946 to proceed to production after expending only $179,000 on exploration, more than $18 million has been required at Detour to achieve the same level of confidence on which to base this decision.
>
> Inflation has significantly affected plant costs. Take Campbell Red Lake again as an example: the total expended to mid-1965 on the mine, townsite, and plant, for an 800 ton per day operation, amounted to $6.4 million. But it will cost us more than $91 million to expand production by a thousand tons a day at the Dome Mine and more than $140 million for the operation at Detour.
>
> Obviously confidence in future gold prices is required to justify investments of this magnitude. Just as obviously, we have that confidence. We look ahead to a continuation of extreme market volatility, but with a gradual increase in the median or average price of gold in the years to come. World economies are not going to change in the foreseeable future and a basic inflation rate of 10 to 12 per cent seems locked in. The role of gold in the monetary system will not decrease, and the future for Timmins and the surrounding gold area is brighter now than it has ever been.

The decision to proceed with the Detour Lake project attracted immediate attention. *The Northern Miner* carried the headline, "Canada's largest gold mine," and stated, "By 1988 it is expected that Detour will be the largest gold producer in Canada in terms of tonnage and the second largest (next to Campbell Red Lake) in terms of gold production."

Further evidence of planned growth for the Dome group of companies was the announcement in late February, 1981, of a "significant gold occurrence" in northwestern Ontario:

Detour Lake Project,
December 1981 —
Camp at Sagimeo Lake
(2 miles from mine site),
housing 450 men. (above)

Foreground: Foundations
for concentrator.
Centre: Foundations for
shops, warehouse, mine dry
complex.
Background: Clearing for
open pit area. (below)

Miner drilling in a stope.

Drilling holes for secondary
blasting at a mill hole.(above)

An electric scoop-tram
dumping at a mill hole.(below)

On February 27, 1981 Dome announced a continuation of a major drilling programme on what appears to be a "significant gold occurrence" at its joint venture project in the Opapimis-kan Lake area approximately 80 miles north of Pickle Lake in northwestern Ontario. Since prospecting commenced on the claims in 1973, a total of $945,000 has been spent on the property and 122 diamond drill holes completed to the end of 1980. Dome and partners plan to spend another $1.8 million on further detailed drilling during 1981. The gold mineralization occurs in a banded iron-formation and preliminary estimates indicate in excess of one million tons grading 0.20 ounces per ton. Numerous other drill intersections on the property require further investigation. Dome Exploration (Canada) Ltd. is the project operator with a 35 per cent participation; the other partners are Canadian Nickel Co. (Inco Ltd.) 23.95 per cent, Esso Minerals Canada Ltd. (Imperial Oil) 23.95 per cent and Lacana Mining Corp. 17.1 per cent.

With the increase in production capacity for the parent mine, and the mining and exploration subsidiaries maintaining a high rate of activity, Dome Mines approached the eighties with optimism. Yet, even though the future appeared bright, a note of warning was sounded by Chairman Matthews in May, 1980:

Caution should be used when interpreting the recent financial results of gold mining companies. The prices of all metals are subject to cyclical swings, and recent history has demonstrated the even more pronounced effect on precious metals. Most gold producers have been operating with antiquated plants and equipment, and sudden large price increases create profit levels which cannot be maintained as we respond to social and economic factors . . .

Matthews reminded Dome shareholders that long-range planning was, "to say the least, difficult and somewhat scary" in the "highly emotional" gold market experienced during January and February of 1980, which "once again demonstrated the high volatility of our commodity." He continued:

The world market for gold will always be very sensitive. The most visible factors are the value of the U.S. dollars *vis-à-vis* harder currencies, the cessation of bullion sales by the U.S. Treasury and the International Monetary Fund, unexpected world events that take on crisis proportions — which I call the fear complex — these over and above the normal world supply-demand characteristics of the market. Unlike the more conventional type of manufacturing or commercial business, the market for our product is beyond our control.

However, a decidedly hopeful note prevailed in the Chairman's predictions of the future progress of Dome Mines after seventy years of production. Gold bullion would have "an increasingly important role, even in its demonetarized state, to play in world commerce and finance." The direction of Dome Mines, which had weathered seven decades, two wars and a world economic depression, was clear: "As our plans are projected out into the mid-eighties, we continue to be confident of the Company's ability to carry out substantial increases in capacity and to deal with the unforeseen difficulties, world-wide, which will inevitably arise in this decade."

Taschereau has with him a strong managerial team to aid him in achieving these ends. Combining mature experience and youthful vigour, this team is well equipped to cope with problems which would inevitably arise. Along with the experience of Bruce Matthews, Taschereau is also assisted by many others who contribute to the successful operation of the Dome group. Fraser M. Fell, who, as Senior Partner of the legal firm of Fasken and Calvin, had carried on in the traditional role of Secretary of the Company in a line unbroken since its inception in 1910, resigned in mid-1981 to accept the newly created position of Vice-Chairman of the Board. The Treasurer from 1977 to 1980, and formerly Office Superintendent at both Campbell and Sigma over a period of forty-three years, Robert B. Hutchison, moved to Toronto upon the retirement of Edmund Andrecheck. (As a matter of interest, Bob Hutchison's father, John, was Office Superintendent at Dome from 1919 to 1928 and at Sigma from 1934 to 1947.) H. Douglas Scharf was Controller from 1978 to 1980, and in 1981, upon the retirement of Hutchison, was appointed Treasurer. At that time, Robert R. Quesnel, formerly Office Superintendent at Dome and with a total service of twelve years, was moved to Toronto as Controller. John W.W. Hick, formerly of Fasken and Calvin, was appointed the first in-house Secretary, a move required to better accommodate the more time-consuming and demanding day-to-day requirements of a growing enterprise. The two executives directly concerned with the running of the mines and with the finding of new sources of ore were C. Henry Brehaut, Vice-President, Operations, and G.S. Wallace Bruce, Vice-President, Exploration. In 1980 Kenneth P. Wright was appointed Chief Metallurgist.

After four years as a Director of Dome and Sigma, Clifford L. Michel, feeling the increasing pressures of other commitments, found it necessary to resign from his positions. Although saddened by his departure, the Directors accepted his decision and welcomed to the Board Alan R. McFarland, Cliff Michel's son-in-law and general partner in the firm of Lazard, Freres and Co., invest-

The senior staff at the South Porcupine plant (left to right):
John Vehkala, Chief Mine Engineer; Ron Colquhoun, Mill Superintendent; Robert Perry, General
Superintendent; Harry Pyke, General Manager; Silvio Torlone, Plant Superintendent; Bill Reid,
Office Superintendent; Dean Rogers, Chief Geologist; Brian Robertson, Mine Superintendent.

ment bankers of New York.

Dome management in the eighties has much to occupy its attention: the major expansions underway at South Porcupine and at Campbell; the development of the significant gold deposit at Detour Lake; a large-scale exploration programme; major interests in Dome Petroleum, and important holdings in Canada Tungsten, Denison and Noranda Mines, and smaller interests in numerous other companies.

Malcolm Taschereau expressed concern about the level of taxation imposed upon the industry to which he has devoted most of his life. At Campbell Red Lake's annual meeting in 1980, he pointed out one of the major stumbling blocks to vigorous and prosperous growth in the mining industry of Ontario:

> The rate of taxation of the mining industry in Ontario compares unfavourably with every other province but one in Canada. Our political leaders have reason to be concerned at the lack of mining investment. However, to say the least, I find it strange that a solution, as proposed in the latest provincial budget, is to provide offsetting grants for mineral exploration to companies and individuals not in the mining industry and excludes the mining companies operating in Ontario. With all its other problems in Quebec, for instance, our level of total taxation for equivalent production would be 10 per cent less and our write-off against taxes for mineral exploration would be 18 per cent greater than in Ontario. This is not to say that taxes are not also too high in Quebec. Small wonder, then, at the lack of investment in new mining ventures.

In June, 1980, he noted that not one new mine of any importance had been brought into production in Ontario since 1971, and that exploration activity was declining. As he told a public affairs conference in Toronto at that time:

> . . . The quality of life in Ontario, which is dependent on a vigorous mining industry is in real jeopardy . . . If the Province of Ontario north of the 46th parallel is to avoid being returned to a vast wasteland inhabited only by a few trappers and fishermen, people must be encouraged to settle there — and people need jobs. Jobs will be created primarily in two industries — forest products and mining. With substantial activity in these areas, other industries will follow. The future of our province lies in the North, and it is up to us to develop policies that will assist.

At the time of this writing (1982), the mining industry as a whole is having serious price problems for its products, and the Dome Mine's group in particular is concerned about short-term gold price trends. However, the President and his associates believe the long-term price trend is upward, over and above the rate of inflation, because of greater industrial usage and broader-based and rising investor demand with only a *moderate* and *diminishing gold* supply expected in the years ahead. They remain conscious of Dome's past achievements, often realized in spite of great adversity, and are justly proud of the sixty-two years of uninterrupted dividends, a record unequalled in the mining industry of Canada.

It is hoped that concern about the future of mining will be contagious and that others may join in trying to re-establish northern Ontario and other parts of northern Canada as centres of forestry and mining acitivites. The resources are there and we have the skills and experience to develop them.

APPENDIX:
Some technical details

General geology of Dome Mine

More than seventy years of continuous mining activity have gradually disclosed the geology and ore deposits in a block of ground approximately two miles long, one mile wide and one mile deep. They have revealed a complex geologic picture with gold-bearing orebodies in several different rock types and in many different structural settings. Most of the major rock types of the Porcupine area are represented in the mine and most of them contain ore.

The Dome Mine lies on the south limb of the Porcupine syncline in an area where the Keewatin rocks are overlain by the Timiskaming series of metasedimentary slate and conglomerate and where the northeasterly plunge of this whole folded assemblage creates the structure locally referred to as the greenstone nose (see Generalized Geology Plan).

South of the sediments lies a zone of magnesium-rich, metamorphosed and carbonatized rocks which trends to the east-northeast and which is presumed to occupy a fault zone associated with a branch of the main Porcupine-Destor Fault. To the west, this highly altered and carbonate rock zone passes between the two major porphyry bodies of the mine, namely, the Paymaster and the Preston porphyries grading to a chloritic and talcose zone before joining with the main Porcupine-Destor Fault. To the east, within the carbonatized zone are found lenses of porphyry-type rocks, similar lithologically to the main porphyry bodies. The eastern extremity of the zone also grades to a chloritic and talcose altered zone before being truncated by the Burrows-Benedict fault.

To the south of the highly altered-porphyry-carbonate rock zone are the south greenstones. They consist of a series of south-dipping massive flows, more mafic than the flows of the greenstone nose. Their anomalous south dip suggests that a major structural break exists along the Porcupine-Destor Fault, which dips steeply north and which is identified by a well marked talc-chlorite zone. This zone passes about three quarters of a mile south of the mine workings.

Classification of the ore deposits

Type I
- Long narrow veins in schist parallel to the general trend of the formations.
    (a) Ankerite veins (in the greenstone nose).
    (b) Quartz-tourmaline veins (chiefly in highly altered rocks).

Type II
- Lenticular or irregular "tension" veins in massive rocks or crossing the schisosity in schistose rocks. They cut Type I veins.
    (a) Orebodies of veins arranged en echelon in massive lavas in the greenstone nose.
    (b) Stockworks, chiefly in the sedimentary trough and generally in conglomerate.
    (c) Stockworks in porphyries and associated highly altered wall rock.

Type III
- Mineralized rock, in which the gold is associated with pyrite and/or pyrrhotite and in which there is little or no vein material.

Type IV
- Silicified greenstone.

Mineralogy of the ore deposits

Gold occurs primarily as coarse native metal in quartz or ankerite-type veins. Several tellurides, namely, altaite, petzite and tellurbismuthite have been recognized in the mine; however, they constitute a very minor source of the total gold production. Silver is recovered as a by-product of the operation, in the ratio of about one ounce silver to six ounces gold.

Sulphides are present in all the ore and average about 2 to 3 per cent. Pyrite and/or pyrrhotite are the dominant sulphides; however, chalcopyrite, sphalerite and galena are found locally in most ore types and are quite good indicators of gold content.

Scheelite is found in minor quantities, predominantly in association with the porphyry ore. In one particular zone in the mine, arsenopyrite is sparsely disseminated in the silicified greenstone-type ore.

Ore genesis

The emplacement of primary lode gold deposits within the mine appears to have taken two forms. Firstly, as a chemically precipitated sediment along with cherty and ferran dolomite (ankerite) beds in a mafic volcanic sequence and secondly, as hydrothermal quartz veins associated with later stage felsic volcanism. The duality of the emplacement process accounts for not only those orebodies which seem to be confined within specific stratigraphic boundaries (e.g. ankerite and tuffaceous-type ore), but for those orebodies which appear to

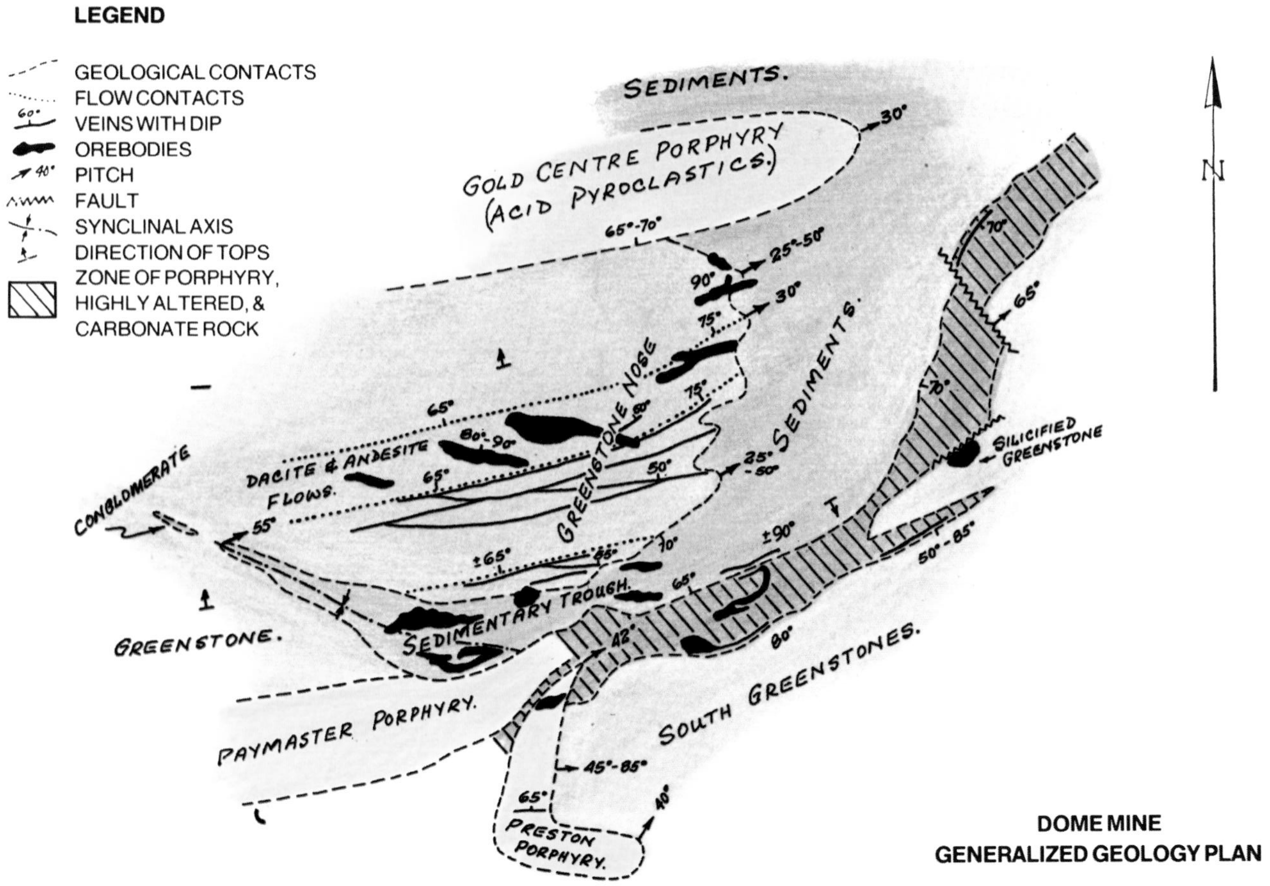

LEGEND

GEOLOGICAL CONTACTS	
FLOW CONTACTS	
VEINS WITH DIP	
OREBODIES	
PITCH	
FAULT	
SYNCLINAL AXIS	
DIRECTION OF TOPS	
ZONE OF PORPHYRY,	
HIGHLY ALTERED, &	
CARBONATE ROCK	

DOME MINE

GENERALIZED GEOLOGY PLAN

SEDIMENTS.

GOLD CENTRE PORPHYRY
(ACID PYROCLASTICS.)

GREENSTONE NOSE.

SEDIMENTS.

DACITE & ANDESITE FLOWS.

SEDIMENTARY TROUGH.

GREENSTONE.

PAYMASTER PORPHYRY.

SOUTH GREENSTONES.

SILICIFIED GREENSTONE.

PRESTON PORPHYRY.

CONGLOMERATE

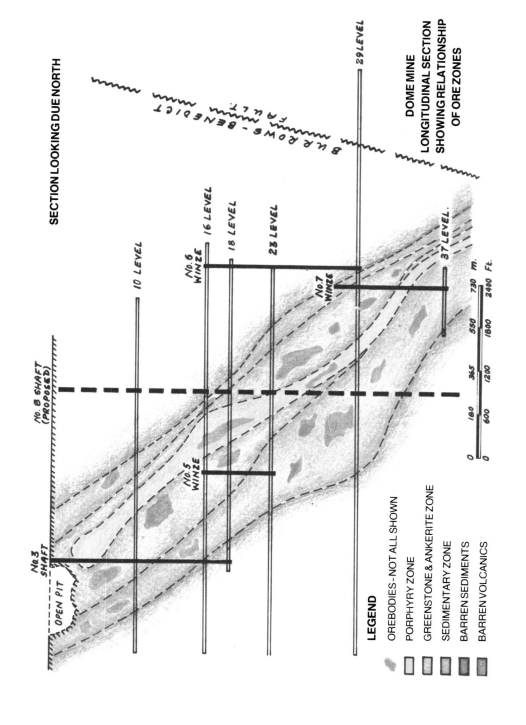

SECTION LOOKING DUE NORTH

BURROWS - BENEDICT FAULT

DOME MINE
LONGITUDINAL SECTION
SHOWING RELATIONSHIP
OF ORE ZONES

No.3 SHAFT
OPEN PIT
No.8 SHAFT (PROPOSED)
10 LEVEL
No.6 WINZE
16 LEVEL
18 LEVEL
23 LEVEL
No.5 WINZE
No.7 WINZE
29 LEVEL
37 LEVEL

730 m.
550
365
180
0
2400 Ft.
1800
1200
600
0

LEGEND

OREBODIES - NOT ALL SHOWN
PORPHYRY ZONE
GREENSTONE & ANKERITE ZONE
SEDIMENTARY ZONE
BARREN SEDIMENTS
BARREN VOLCANICS

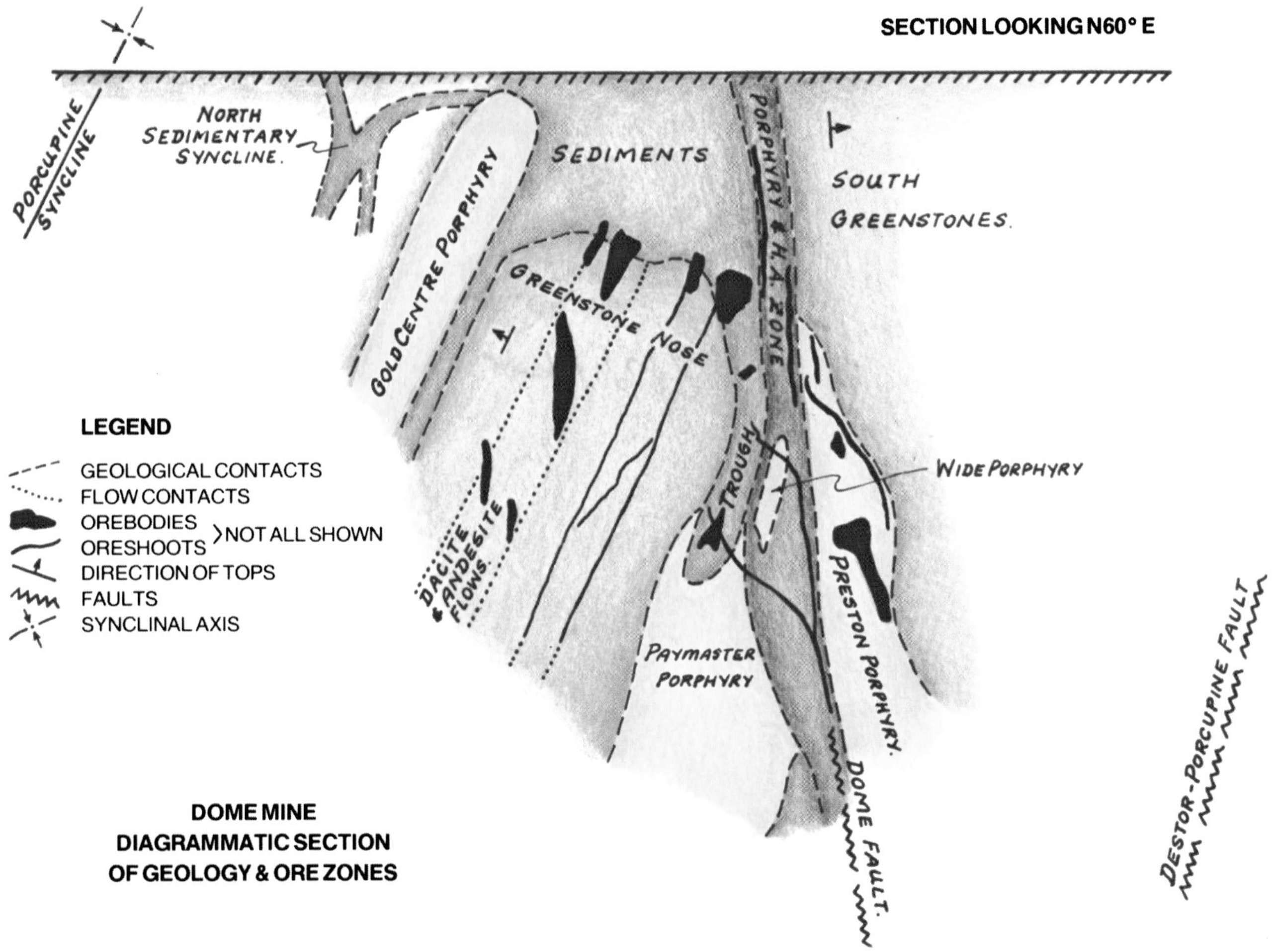

SECTION LOOKING N 60° E

SOUTH GREENSTONES.

DESTOR-PORCUPINE FAULT

WIDE PORPHYRY

PRESTON PORPHYRY.

DOME FAULT.

PORPHYRY & H.A. ZONE

TROUGH

PAYMASTER PORPHYRY

SEDIMENTS

GREENSTONE NOSE

DACITE & ANDESITE FLOWS

GOLDCENTRE PORPHYRY

NORTH SEDIMENTARY SYNCLINE.

PORCUPINE SYNCLINE

LEGEND

GEOLOGICAL CONTACTS
FLOW CONTACTS
OREBODIES ⟩ NOT ALL SHOWN
ORESHOOTS ⟩
DIRECTION OF TOPS
FAULTS
SYNCLINAL AXIS

DOME MINE
DIAGRAMMATIC SECTION
OF GEOLOGY & ORE ZONES

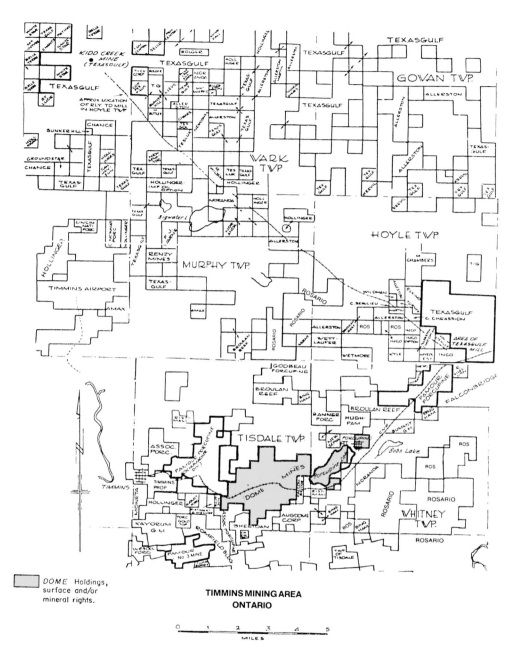

**TIMMINS MINING AREA
ONTARIO**

DOME Holdings, surface and/or mineral rights.

0 1 2 3 4 5
MILES

Courtesy of the *Northern Miner Press,*
Canadian Mines Handbook, 1981

be an expression of the tectonic process from which they were formed. Examples of ore deposits which are structurally controlled include the deposits of the highly altered-carbonate rock zone, the long sinuous quartz-tourmaline veins associated with drag folding in the porphyries, and the fracture filling emplacement of auriferous quartz veins in the dacite-type ore.

At least three ages of quartz veins have been found to contain gold mineralization, while at least two other quartz carbonate vein systems appear to be post-ore. In addition to the multi-stage nature of the gold mineralization, it is acknowledged that remobilization of some of the gold has taken place as well. The effect of this remobilization and the processes which were responsible for it have had a marked influence on the ores and, more particularly, on those within the sedimentary environment. Primary sedimentary features, however, have been all but masked by later tectonic deformation.

In reality, the gold mineralization at the Dome has been shown to be spatially related to the two most significant "structural" features within the mine, namely the greenstone nose and the highly altered zone. Quite paradoxically, the former may represent the expression of an erosional surface, while the latter may have been formerly an ultrabasic flow.

References

1925 Burrows A.G.
The Porcupine Gold Area (Fourth Report); Ontario Department of Mines Vol. XXXIII 1924, pp. 72-76 (Dome).

1944 Holmes T.C.
Some Porphyry-Sediment Contacts at the Dome Mine, Ontario; Economic Geology Vol. XXXIX 1944 pp. 133-141.

1947 Holmes T.C.
Structural Control of Ore Deposits at the Dome Mine; Canadian Institute of Mining and Metallurgy. Transactions Vol. L 1947 pp. 283-297.

1948 Holmes T.C.
Dome Mine, Structural Geology of Canadian Ore Deposits, Canadian Institute of Mining and Metallurgy 1948 pp. 539-547.

1964 Holmes T.C.
Dome Mine, Geology of Mining Properties in Tisdale Township, Porcupine Area, Ontario Department of Mines, P.R. 1964-5, pp. 28-49.

1964 Ferguson S.A. (and associated geologists).
Geology of Mining Properties in Tisdale Township, Porcupine Area, Ontario Department of Mines, P.R. 1964-5.

1968 Ferguson S.A. (and associated geologists).
Geology and Ore Deposits of Tisdale Township, District of Cochrane;

Ontario Department of Mines, Geological Report 58, 1968.

1968 Holmes T.C.

Dome Mine, Geology and Ore Deposits of Tisdale Township, Ontario Department of Mines, G.R. 58, 1968, pp. 82-98.

1979 Bell D.R. and Rogers D.S.

A Problem Related to Outlining Gold Deposits along the Greenstone Nose at the Dome Mine, South Porcupine, Ontario. Presented at the 81st C.I.M.M. Annual General Meeting, Montreal, Que. 1979.

1979 Freyer B.J., Kerrich R., Hutchinson R.W., Pierce M.G., Rogers D.S.

Archean Precious-Metal Hydrothermal Systems, Dome Mine, Abitibi Greenstone Belt I Patterns of Alteration and Metal Distribution. Canadian Journal of Earth Sciences Vol. 16 pp. 421-439.

A short description follows of some of the more important ore types currently being mined (1982).

Ankerite veins

The importance of these veins is mentioned in connection with the history of mine development. The main veins lie in schisted greenstones, within a series of spherulitic flows referred to locally as the Vipond group (andesite, spherulitic, key flow, broken spherulitic, 99 flow and lower spherulitic). Some follow flow contacts quite closely; others cross the flows at small angles and tend to have flatter dips. The main ankerite veins extend east and west of No. 3 shaft. Eastward, and at the tops of the orebodies, they encounter sediments and may extend as quartz stringers through the contact for short distances. A number of these veins have been mined east to the sediments and west to a diabase dyke, and have provided a good source of ore from the 18th level to the 7th level for over thirty-five years.

Some of these veins were developed west of the diabase on several levels above the 16th, and on selected levels below the 16th, namely the 18th, 23rd, and 29th, and gradually extended some 2,500 feet to the west boundaries of the property. Generally, the veins and other geological features were found in the locations expected, but the tonnage and grades were lower than those above the 16th level east of No. 3 shaft. As most of this work was done when the price of gold was $35.00 per ounce, little stoping was undertaken on these veins. With current (1982) gold prices substantially higher and with newer mining techniques for narrow veins, the ore potential of the west end of the mine is excellent.

It is of interest to note that the diabase is generally considered to be later than the greenstones and the vein structures, and should have no effect on the grade on either side of the dyke.

Quartz tourmaline

Lying between the sediments and the south greenstones, and east of the north end of the Preston porphyry, there is a zone of rocks mapped as porphyry, carbonate rock and "highly altered" rocks. In the geological mapping prior to 1940, these zones were noted as porphyry and carbonate, but it was found convenient, in later exploration, to introduce a new term of "highly altered" rocks to cover other rocks within the zone, too altered to permit underground identification as either porphyry or carbonate rock. These rocks contain varying amounts of fuchsite, which imparts a characteristic and distinctive green colour to the rock type "highly altered."

Several orebodies, with dimensions of up to 600 feet by 12 feet, extend vertically for three or four levels (600 feet), consist of quartz-tourmaline veins, and occur in both highly altered rocks and in porphyry. They consist of a white quartz vein with light brown tourmaline bands parallel to the walls of the vein. Occasionally, ore is found in the walls of the main vein and it is common for the vein to roll sharply parallel to the pitch. This latter condition complicates grade control in mining but, fortunately, the grade is good. The principal veins of this type have been mined from the 14th, 16th, 24th and 28th levels.

Fuchsite ore

A trough of Timiskaming sediments, locally referred to as the north syncline, lies north of the gold centre porphyry which, in turn, lies north of the greenstone nose. These sediments were drilled from surface and explored on the 12th level with encouraging results. Later exploration was done on the 10th and 15th levels to outline the extensions of the new orebody. However, the cross-cut on the 12th level, to investigate the north syncline, cut the west end of the fuchsite vein, which has since been opened up from the 8th to the 17th levels (1,400 feet). The main orebody is 500 feet in length, 10 feet in width, and is of considerably higher grade than the average ore in the mine. Eight diamond drill holes had cut through the rich central part of the vein, in previous work, without yielding an assay of interest. The vein lies mainly in carbonate rock, indistinguishable from that which is common in most of the mine, and in which work done up to that time had given little indication of being favourable for hosting orebodies.

The grey to white quartz veins contain streaks and patches of fuchsite throughout. Numerous barren quartz veins lacking fuchsite lie in the walls at many places. Exploration east, along the extension of the main fuchsite zone, has located two similar banded fuchsite sections but, for the most part, has encountered difficult ground conditions where the zone grades to incompetent talcose rocks.

Dacite ore

The dacite is one of a series of flows lying north of the sedimentary trough which dips north about 65 degrees. The dacite orebodies lie in this flow and the adjacent flow to the south, the andesite, with a total thickness of about 300 feet. The orebodies are vertical within the flow and consist of en echelon quartz veins extending at shallow angles across the strike of the zone. The dacite and andesite within the ore zones are bleached compared with their normal colour and are usually mineralized with pyrrhotite and pyrite. The ore zones are large and may be up to 800 feet by 75 feet in area and extend through four or five levels (750 feet). They occur plentifully from the 7th to the 19th levels (1,800 feet).

The dacite ore is excellent grade and usually considerable free gold is evident throughout the ore zone as finely disseminated, coarse veinlets and massive patches within the quartz and adjoining bleached greenstone.

Quartz porphyry

From commencement of operations until the early thirties, porphyry was considered to be an unfavourable host rock and exploration avoided it. However, at about this time, work at Preston East Dome, south of the Dome workings, met with success in the south part of the Preston porphyry. Later they found ore in other porphyry bodies throughout the mine and in greenstone around these bodies, in what Dome geologists referred to as the porphyry greenstones, i.e. south of the sedimentary trough.

At Dome, a long exploration drive to the south in 1940, through a favourable silicified greenstone, cut good grade ore in the northeast tip of the Preston porphyry. This ore extended for three levels and following this success, a search of the porphyry found a number of substantial orebodies on various levels. Some were in the same place on the geological structure, while others were found, by diamond drilling, to places where ore projected downward on pitch both from Dome and Preston workings. The good relationship which prevailed between the managements and staff of both companies was mutually beneficial, and several joint programmes were undertaken.

In 1953-54, the 23rd level was driven south to the projection of a zone from Preston to Dome in the footwall of the Preston porphyry. It was a long drive and the results at the projected target were disappointing. In 1966-67, a drive on the 25th level to the Preston porphyry, and subsequent diamond drilling in the target area, produced long, low-grade sections of ore. Work above this zone up to the 23rd level cut several other similar sections over the next decade.

In this area, greenstone is more sericitic and grades into what is mapped as porphyry. Flow structure is absent and many of the zones could well be altered intrusives. Gold values and quartz are the main criteria and, with the increase in gold price, this host rock has become a substantial producer of ore at Dome.

Development of the mine

The early development of the mine has been covered in the first few chapters.

Until the late twenties, all the ore in the mine was in sediments and could be roughly divided into two groups of orebodies. One group of quite large bodies extended downward from the surface showings to the 7th level on a northeasterly pitch of about 40 degrees following the greenstone nose which underlay the ore. Mining in these was completed before 1940. Exploration for other orebodies on the greenstone nose has continued intermittently by short diamond drill holes. A few orebodies have been found but, to date, they are all much smaller than those above the 7th level. One of these, on the 24th level, was notable for an almost complete absence of quartz and pyrite, but had scattered high assays with very little between these values.

The other group extended downward on a steep southerly dip from the vicinity of the surface showings. These orebodies occurred irregularly, distributed through the sedimentary trough — a narrow, wedge-shaped block which tapers both westward and downward at approximately 45 degrees towards the east. In the early twenties, a sudden narrowing of this trough near the 12th level alarmed the management, but further drilling indicated that it had retained its normal shape and the favourable sediments continued downward, but narrower than on the upper levels. By the late twenties, it had been followed to the 18th level, about 2,300 feet below surface, where its size and the amount of ore in it were greatly reduced.

The narrowing of this zone called for a search for a new ore zone. The No. 5 winze was sunk from the 16th to the 23rd level and an exploration drive was put out a few hundred feet to look for ore below the sedimentary trough, but without much success. It found a large zone of quartz porphyry (later determined to be the downward extension of the Paymaster porphyry on its normal pitch) where sediments were expected. At this time, porphyry was considered to be an unfavourable host rock and exploration was limited. This programme was probably incomplete when signs of the new zone required came from a different part of the mine.

About five years before this, two exploratory holes into the greenstone north of the sedimentary trough had cut long sections with fair amounts of quartz, but values were low, with only a few high erratics. Following the current practice, the high values were cut to half an ounce and the resulting cut average was quite low. Despite this, crosscuts were driven and boxholes placed. Unfortunately, this work had cut the tops of orebodies but this was not realized at the time. During the following years, about one similar drill intersection a year was obtained, but it was not until one with an unusual number of high erratics was found that another cross-cut was driven. This met with such spectacular success that all other old similar intersections were immediately resampled and tested, with success in almost every case. This zone is now known as the dacite zone and is the host rock of the rich ore on the former Schumacher claims — it is about 300 feet thick and orebodies occur in it plentifully from the 7th to the 19th levels.

When the importance of the dacite ore zone was realized, it was projected to the 23rd level horizon and that level driven from No. 5 winze to a point approximately 3,000 feet from the shaft. Results were disappointing but, two years later, a hole drilled from near the end of this heading cut 118 feet of ore to the south in the sedimentary trough. It then became apparent that the sedimentary trough rakes east at only 45 degrees (much flatter than originally thought), and the previous work from the bottom of No. 5 winze was laid out without allowing sufficiently for this flat rake.

A cross-cut was driven to the intersection and found much less than expected from the drill hole, which was a short distance below the level. A small winze (2,309 winze) was then sunk and four levels developed from it in the mid-thirties. This showed the drill intersection to be a thick, flat piece of ore with substantial bodies of irregular shapes (known as the 2403 group) extending downward from it for up to 500 feet in various directions and dips. This discovery was hailed as a new mine and in 1937-38, No. 6 internal shaft, a counterpart of No. 3, was sunk from the 16th level to the 29th level (2,000 feet to 4,000 feet from surface). It is located 4,800 feet northeast of No. 3 shaft.

This shaft is located well southeast of any known ore zone, so as to avoid tying up ore in the shaft pillar, as had happened previously at No. 3 shaft. The cross-cut on the 16th level to reach the proposed shaft site cut a quartz tourmaline vein in a hitherto unexplored area. This has turned into a substantial producer and others like it have been found since, in similar geologic settings.

Locating No. 6 shaft in this area has proved to be a mixed blessing. Certainly no ore is tied up in the shaft pillar, but a substantial body of extremely incompetent talc rock has been found to occur a short distance below the bottom. Therefore, further sinking will be costly and may not be practical. The first suggestion of this body was found while the hoist room for No. 6 shaft was being excavated. Two drill holes on the 27th level, several hundred feet northeast of the shaft site, cut a talcose zone striking toward the site. It was decided, at the time, that the chance of the zone reaching the shaft site at depth did not warrant interrupting the sinking programme to determine if it would interfere with the shaft, and the programme was continued. The zone did reach the shaft site and sinking had to be stopped above the original target depth. The bottom of the shaft (29th level) is 100 feet below the 28th level.

Up to 1940, all underground mining was shrinkage. In the early years, it was the practice to make the initial opening between levels in any orebody by sinking a winze 60 feet and driving a raise to its bottom. Apparently this was to save carrying the heavy piston machines, then used for drilling, up a long raise. It was easier to muck the winze and lower the machines with the hoist than carry them too far up a raise.

At first, sill recovery of shrinkage stopes was done by drilling off with conventional or slightly longer steel from the drift and from the muck in the stope below. As mining progressed to greater depths, the thin sill pillars were difficult to maintain and, in 1940, diamond drill blast holes up to 75 feet in length were resorted to, with considerable success. In some of the large dacite orebodies in the deeper part of the zone, when the stope was approximately halfway to the next level, loose ground became such a problem that mining was stopped and the thick sill recovered by diamond drill blast holes fanned out from the level above. In due course, other techniques for long hole drilling were adopted as newer machines and steel became available.

The 2403 group of orebodies is large, complex in shape, but excellent grade. Before mining had progressed very far, it was found necessary to undertake a great deal of detailed diamond drilling, which found many unsuspected pieces of ore and resulted in mining plans being substantially changed. The original sill drifts above the 24th level were found to be in the centre of a flat and thick ore zone, which was not suitable for shrinkage mining.

Cut and fill stoping was commenced in the mine in 1940 and, as the complex nature of the 2403 group of orebodies unfolded, it became an obvious method to employ. It was decided to start at the bottom of each branch of ore, in an appropriate mining sequence, and work up through the levels above to the top, thus saving the problems of sill recovery. By the time stoping reached the wider parts of the orebody, modern long hole techniques had been developed and were used to advantage.

The above orebodies are located in the wide porphyry, a quartz-porphyry zone adjacent to the sedimentary trough. This porphyry has been traced from the 13th to the 29th level and detailed work has led to another important complex of orebodies from the 13th to 18th levels, grouped around the same wide porphyry as the 2403 group.

There is an important series of ankerite veins in the mine. They are long, narrow, predominantly grey veins containing ankerite and grey and white quartz, quite unlike the wide, irregular bodies with numerous white quartz veins or mineralized conglomerate which made up all the Dome ore for the first twenty-five years. The most prolific ankerites lie between the sedimentary trough and the dacite ore, and were cut by the cross-cuts and drill holes which found that ore. In most of the early diamond drilling it was the practice to assay all the core, but if the core appeared barren, sections up to thirty or forty feet were taken as one sample. The colour of the ankerites was not much different from the greenstone walls, and they were often overlooked in logging the core. (When included in long sections of waste, the assay was not high enough to attract attention.) When cut by the various cross-cuts, the ankerites were mapped and sampled, but the grade was not sufficiently attractive, at the old price of gold, ($20.67 per oz.) to permit mining at that time. Besides, the development of the large and rich new dacite orebodies occupied the mine's main attention for many years after their discovery. Hence, it was ten years after the first cross-cut exposed an ankerite vein, that mining of these veins commenced. In this interval, the price of gold advanced from $20.67 to $35.00 per oz., which made mining these veins more attractive.

The first large ankerite orebodies developed proved to be tabular masses about 2,000 feet long and 2,000 feet high, rarely more than six feet wide and dipping about 65 degrees north. They were roughly parallel, and 100 feet or less apart, with a few veins crossing from one to the other at small angles to the main vein. They did not come within 500 feet of surface. Shrinkage was the only stoping method used when mining of these orebodies commenced, and dilution from the hanging wall was excessive. Accordingly, cut and fill mining was introduced, using mine waste rock and later pit sand, as backfill; since 1957, hydraulic filling, using classified mill tailings, has replaced pit sand.

Gradually, the use of cut and fill stoping expanded until most current stopes were being filled. Shrinkage stoping is used in a few places where ground conditions permit. It has the advantages of being cheaper, faster, and of creating a broken ore reserve for use in smoothing out the inevitable "feast" and "famine" in production from cut and fill stopes. Where dilution is not high enough to offset these considerations, it is usually the more economic method.

Commencing in 1970, the use of trackless load-haul-dump units (diesel and electric) and drill jumbos for panel cut and fill stopes and longhole stopes, in both wide and narrow orebodies, have brought about tremendous improvements in mining techniques and efficiencies.

In many of the wide orebodies at Dome, the veins strike across the stope and end at varying distances from the middle. They usually get narrower going into the walls. In shrinkage stoping in the early years, there came a time when the veins going into the walls did not justify further slashing. Pockets of high-grade ore are apt to occur in small, inconspicuous stringers in the ends of veins. As such orebodies have been mined through several levels, thousands of tons have caved from the walls of the old shrinkage stopes, providing muck which is worth milling, due to the gold in these small stringers left in the walls. Its effect on costs over the years has been decidedly favourable.

No. 6 shaft was completed in 1938, and opened up sufficient new zones for development and mining that it was not until 1960 that consideration was given to further sinking. The possibility of sinking No. 6 shaft was investigated by several drill holes from near the shaft bottom. None of these holes was able to penetrate more than a few hundred feet into the talc zone previously mentioned, despite using special bits and drilling methods. They did, however, indicate that the talc zone became steadily less competent, and thoughts of sinking in this area were abandoned.

Accordingly, a new shaft, No. 7, was located 1,245 feet northwest from No. 6 shaft. The site was extensively tested by drilling before sinking commenced, but the results, while favourable, were inconclusive, due to the excessive wandering of the long drill holes. The shaft was collared at the 27th level horizon (3,641 feet from surface), and was completed in 1963 at a depth of 5,263 feet. The lowest level of the mine, at the present time (1982), is the 37th at a depth of 5,084 feet from surface.

Diamond drilling and development work on the new levels found ore in the ankerite veins and some good values in light-coloured sericitic rock lying along the sedimentary trough, which may be the downward projection of the wide porphyry. The sedimentary trough has narrowed appreciably at these horizons.

Exploration diamond drilling found scattered values over considerable widths in a mineralized area well below the 37th or bottom level.

Stoping and development raising were commenced on some of these zones but, in 1971, due to labour shortages, the then prevailing price of gold, and rapidly rising costs, further work at No. 7 shaft was suspended and the workings allowed to fill with water.

In 1980, with gold prices at unprecedented levels, some improvement in the availability of labour, and the introduction of new mining techniques, plans were made to de-water the shaft and resume mining operations. This work was completed in 1981, and development in known ore zones and to the projected No. 8 shaft area on two levels was underway in 1982.

A GLOSSARY OF MINING TERMINOLOGY

(Based on the glossary of Mining Explained, *Northern Miner Press Limited.)*

adit A passageway or opening driven horizontally into the side of a hill, generally for the purpose of exploring or otherwise opening a mineral deposit. Strictly speaking, an adit differs from a tunnel in that it is open to the atmosphere at one end, whereas a tunnel is open at both ends.

agitation In metallurgy, the act or state of being stirred or shaken mechanically, sometimes accompanied by the introduction of compressed air.

alteration Any physical or chemical change in a rock or mineral subsequent to its formation.

ankerite veins A term referring to a series of magnesium and iron-rich carbonate veins which occur in tabular form along the contacts of selective volcanic flow units. White quartz is present in many of the ankerite veins as irregular patches, and, in some cases, as a ladder structure which does not penetrate the wall rock. In addition to the quartz, these veins also contain patchy black tourmalene and from one to three per cent finely disseminated pyrite and pyrrhotite; free gold is not common in this ore type.

anomaly A term applied to a departure from the normal or field characteristic, commonly used in geophysical prospecting. Thus, in a magnetometer survey an area showing much higher (or much lower) readings of magnetic intensity than the surrounding area would be identified as an anomaly.

assay To test ores or minerals by chemical or other methods for the purpose of determining the amount of valuable metals contained.

assessment work The amount of work specified by law, which must be done each year to retain legal control of mining lands.

autogenous grinding The process of grinding in a rotating steel drum which uses, as a grinding medium large pieces or pebbles of the ore being ground, instead of conventional steel balls or rods.

backstope The initial lift or slice when commencing to stope or mine from a drift.

base metal A term generally applied to the commercial metals such as iron,

	copper, lead and zinc, as distinct from the precious metals (gold, silver, platinum, etc.).
blast furnace	A metallurgical furnace in which mixed charges of ores, fluxes, and fuels are blown with a continuous blast of hot air and oxygen-enriched air for the chemical reduction of metals to their metallic state. Iron ore is most commonly treated in this way, as well as some ores of copper and lead.
blast-hole stoping	The use of long holes (usually 15 to 100 feet) fanning out from a drill, set-up in a carefully engineered layout, in a large orebody to be later loaded with explosives and blasted. The holes are usually percussion-drilled with sectional steel rods and tungsten carbide tipped bits, but diamond drill holes may also be used.
bullion	Precious metal in bars, ingots or other uncoined form.
by-product	A secondary or additional mineral or mineral product.
cage	The conveyance used to transport men and equipment in a shaft.
carbon-in-pulp process (C.I.P.)	This process is used to recover gold that has been dissolved in cyanide leach agitators. It differs from the Merrill-Crowe recovery process in that no liquid-solid separation is necessary. Pulp, after cyanidation, is contacted in a series of agitators with coarse activated carbon particles. The carbon is moved counter-current to the pulp, absorbing more gold as it passes through the circuit. Loaded carbon is removed by screening from the first agitator. Gold is recovered from the loaded carbon by stripping at elevated temperature and pressure in a caustic cyanide solution. This high-grade solution is then passed through an electrolytic cell, where gold is deposited on a steel wool cathode, which is later smelted to produce Doré (gold-silver) bullion. Stripped carbon is reactivated in a kiln and returned to the C.I.P. circuit.
chalcopyrite	A sulphide mineral of copper and iron, being a common ore of copper.
chute	An inclined opening, usually constructed of timber and equipped with a gate or stop-log, through which ore is drawn from a stope into mine cars.
claim	A portion of mining land held under federal or provincial law. The common size is 1,320 feet square, containing 40 acres.
collar	The term applied to the timbering or concrete around the mouth of a shaft; also used to describe the top of a drill hole.
compressor	A machine for compressing air to a pressure sufficient to actuate mine machinery.
concentrate	A product containing the valuable metal and from which most of the waste material in the ore has been eliminated.
concentrator	A particular type of milling plant that produces a concentrate of the valuable minerals or metals. The concentrate must then be treated in some other type of plant, such as a smelter, to effect

	recovery of the pure metal.
conglomerate	A sedimentary rock consisting of rounded, waterworn pebbles or boulders compacted together into a solid mass.
contact	The line or plane along which two different rocks come together.
core	The long cylinder of rock, about one inch or more in diameter, that is recovered by the diamond drill.
cross-cut	A horizontal opening driven across the course of a vein or structure, or in general across the strike of the rock formation; a connection from a shaft to an ore structure.
crusher	A machine for crushing rock, such as a gyratory crusher, jaw crusher, stamp mill, etc.
cut-and-fill	A method of stoping in which ore is removed in slices, or lifts, following which the excavation is filled with rock or other waste material known as backfill, before the subsequent slice is mined, the backfill supports the walls of the stope.
cyanidation	A method of extracting gold or silver by dissolving it in a weak solution of sodium or potassium cyanide.
decline	An inclined shaft, ramp or passageway driven at a shallow angle downward (usually -10 to -20 degrees) for entry into a mine. Transportation for men, material and rock is usually by rubber-tired vehicles.
development	The underground work carried out for the purpose of reaching and opening up a mineral deposit, which includes shaft sinking, cross-cutting, drifting and raising.
diamond drill	A rotary type of rock drill in which the cutting is done by abrasion rather than percussion. The cutting bit is set with industrial grade diamonds and is attached to the end of long, hollow rods through which water is pumped to the cutting face. The drill cuts a core of rock which is recovered in long, cylindrical sections, an inch or more in diameter.
dike	A long and relatively thin body of igneous rock that, while in the molten state, has intruded a fissure in older rocks and solidified.
dilution	Waste or low grade rock which is unavoidably removed along with the ore in the mining process.
dip	The angle at which a vein, structure or rock bed is inclined from the horizontal, measured at right angles to the strike.
disseminated ore	Ore carrying small particles of valuable minerals, spread more or less uniformly through the gangue matter; distinct from massive ore, wherein the valuable minerals occur in almost solid form with very little waste material included.
drift (drive)	A horizontal passage underground that follows along the length of a vein or rock formation as opposed to a cross-cut which crosses the rock formation.

exploration	The prospecting, diamond drilling and other work involved in searching for ore.
face	As applied to a drift, cross-cut or stope, is the end in which work is progressing.
fault	A break in the earth's crust caused by forces which have moved the rock on one side with respect to the other; faults may extend for miles, or be only a few inches in length; similarly, the movement or displacement along the fault may vary widely; ore deposits are commonly associated with faults, as the movement frequently provides a channel for the passage of ore-bearing solutions.
feeder	A mechanical device, usually automatic, for a regular and controlled supply of process materials to a machine; also applies to the controlled feeding of reagents to processes.
ferrous	Containing iron.
fine gold	Almost pure gold. Fineness is the proportion of pure gold or silver in jewellery or bullion expressed in parts per thousand. Thus, 925 fine gold indicates 925 parts out of 1,000, or 92.5 per cent pure gold.
fissure	An extensive crack, break or fracture in rocks.
float	Pieces of rock that have been broken off and moved from their original locations by natural forces such as frost action or glaciers.
flotation	A milling process by which some mineral particles are induced to become attached to bubbles of froth and float, and others to sink. In this way the valuable minerals are concentrated and separated from the worthless gangue.
flux	Used in metallurgical smelting of ore and concentrate. It is usually a salt or other mineral, such as sodium carbonate, borax or silica, and is used to assist in the purification of metals by fusion of the impurities into a slag.
fold	Any bending or wrinkling of rock strata.
footwall	The wall or rock on the underside of a dipping vein or ore structure.
fracture	As the name implies, a break in the rock. The opening affords the opportunity for entry of mineral-bearing solutions. A cross-fracture is a minor break extending at more or less right angles to the direction of the principal fractures.
free milling	A term usually applied to ores of gold or silver from which the precious metals can be recovered by concentrating methods, without resorting to roasting or chemical treatment.
gangue	The worthless minerals or rock associated with valuable minerals in an ore deposit.
geology	The science concerned with the study of the rocks which compose the earth.

geophysics	A scientific method of prospecting that utilizes the physical properties of minerals to detect their presence. Common properties include magnetism, specific gravity, electrical conductivity, radioactivity, and sound wave reflections.
glory hole	A large, open pit from which ore is extracted, especially where broken ore is passed to underground workings before being hoisted to surface.
grubstake	Finances or supplies of food, tools, etc., furnished a prospector on promise of some share in any discoveries he makes.
hand cobbing	Separation of rich ore from the gangue or worthless material by hand. Ore may be spread on a slow-moving belt and a picker then makes the separation.
hoist	The machine used for raising and lowering the cage or other conveyance in a shaft.
industrial minerals	Usually non-metallic minerals which are used in industry and manufacturing processes in their natural state, though with some beneficiation to imposed specifications; examples include asbestos, salt, feldspar, gravels, silica and talc.
intrusive	A body of igneous rock formed by the consolidation of magma intruded into other rocks, in contrast to lavas, which are extruded upon the surface.
leaching	A chemical process used in milling for the extraction of valuable minerals from ore; also, the natural process by which ground waters dissolve minerals, thus leaving the rock with a smaller proportion of some of the minerals than it contained originally.
lens	Generally used to describe a body of ore that is thick in the middle and tapers towards the ends.
lenticular	A lens-shaped deposit having roughly the form of a double convex lens.
level	The horizontal passages on a working horizon in a mine. It is customary to work mines from a shaft, establishing levels at regular intervals, generally 100-150 feet or more apart.
line drive	A horizontal opening which follows a straight course, in contrast to following along the strike of a vein.
long ton	A metric weight of 2,240 pounds avoirdupois.
magnetometer	A sensitive instrument used to measure the magnetic attraction of underlying rocks.
marginal ore deposits	Orebodies whose mineral content approach the lowest limits of commercial workability.
metallurgy	The science concerned with the separation of minerals from their ores and final refining to produce a commercial product or grade.
mill	(a) A plant in which ore is treated for the recovery of valuable metals, or concentration of the valuable minerals into a smaller bulk for shipment to a smelter and other reduction works;

	(b) A machine consisting of a revolving drum, usually containing steel balls or rods, for the fine grinding of ores as a preparation for treatment.
milling ore	Ore that contains sufficient valuable mineral to be treated by milling process.
mineral	A naturally occurring homogeneous substance, having definite physical properties and chemical composition and, if formed under favourable conditions, a definite crystal form.
muskeg	Decayed vegetable matter and black soil forming swampy areas.
nugget	A water-worn piece of precious metal, usually implying some size.
ore	A mixture of ore minerals and gangue from which at least one of the metals can be extracted at a profit.
ore reserves	The prime measured assets of a mine as to tonnage and grade. They may be classified as *positive* or *proven, probable,* or *possible,* in decreasing degree of statistical confidence as to the accuracy of their expressed grade or grades; other terms frequently applied include: *measured, indicated, pillar ore, broken.*
outcrop	An exposure of rock or a mineral deposit that can be seen on surface, i.e. is not covered by water or overburden.
overburden	Worthless, unconsolidated surface material, such as earth, sand and boulders, covering the rock surface.
oxidation	A chemical reaction caused by natural forces that results in a change in the composition of a mineral.
pan	To wash sand, gravel or ground rock in a pan to separate gold or other valuable metals.
pitchblende	An important uranium ore mineral, containing a high percentage of uranium oxide. It is black in colour, possesses a characteristic pitch-like or greasy lustre, and is highly radioactive.
placer	An alluvial deposit of sand and gravel containing valuable minerals such as gold, tin, etc.
plant	A group of buildings, and especially their contained equipment, in which a process or function is carried out; on a mine it will include warehouses, hoisting equipment, compressors, repair shops, offices, mill or concentrator.
porphyry	Any igneous rock in which relatively large, conspicuous crystals (called phenocrysts) are set in a fine-grained groundmass.
pyrite	A hard, heavy, shiny, yellow mineral, being a sulphide of iron. It is a common sulphide, sometimes known as "fool's gold."
pyrrhotite	A less common iron sulphide than pyrite, being a peculiar bronze in colour and magnetic; it is sometimes associated with nickel, in which case it may be mined as a nickel ore.
radioactivity	The property of spontaneously emitting alpha, beta or gamma rays by the disintegration of the nuclei of atoms.

raise	A vertical or inclined underground working that has been excavated from the bottom upward.
reconnaissance	A preliminary examination survey of ground.
recovery	The percentage of valuable mineral in the ore that is recovered by metallurgical treatment.
replacement orebody	An orebody formed by a process during which certain minerals have passed into solution and have been carried away, while valuable minerals from the solution have been deposited in place of those removed.
roasting	The treatment of ore by heat and air, or oxygen-enriched air, in order to remove sulphur and arsenic.
rock	Any naturally formed combination of minerals forming an appreciable part of the earth's crust.
sample	A small portion of rock or mineral deposit, usually taken for the purpose of being assayed to determine possible content of valuable elements.
sampling	Selecting a fractional but representative part of a deposit for analysis.
schist	A foliated metamorphic rock whose grains have a roughly parallel arrangement; it is generally developed by shearing.
seismic prospecting	A geophysical method of prospecting, utilizing the knowledge of the speed and reflection of sound waves in rock.
shaft	A vertical or inclined excavation for the purpose of opening and servicing a mine. It is usually equipped with a hoist at the top, which lowers and raises a conveyance for handling men and material.
shear or shearing	The deformation of rocks by lateral movement along innumerable parallel planes, generally resulting from pressure and producing such metamorphic structures as cleavage and schistosity.
shear zone	A zone in which shearing has occurred on a large scale.
short ton	A weight of 2,000 pounds avoirdupois.
shrinkage stope	A method of stoping which utilizes part of the broken ore as a working floor and as support for the walls.
sill	An intrusive sheet of igneous rock of approximately uniform thickness and generally extending over a considerable lateral extent; it has been forced between level, or gently inclined, beds.
skip	A self-dumping type of bucket or box used in a shaft for hoisting ore or rock.
stamps	Used in a stamp mill. An early method of grinding ore, whereby a heavy hardened-steel rod is raised vertically by a cam mechanism, falling on a steel plate over which an ore slurry is flowing. The particles of ore are ground to the required fineness in preparation for further treatment.
station	An enlargement of a shaft made at the level horizon used primarily for the storage and handling of equipment.

stock pile	Broken ore accumulated in a heap on surface, pending treatment or shipment.
stope	An excavation in a mine from which ore is being or has been extracted.
strike	The direction, or course or bearing, of a vein or rock formation measured on a level surface.
stringer	A narrow vein or irregular filament of mineral traversing a rock mass.
strip	To remove the overburden or barren rock overlying an orebody.
sub-level	An intermediate level or working horizon in a mine opened between main working levels.
sulphide	A compound of sulphur and other elements to form minerals.
tailings	Material rejected from a mill after the recoverable valuable minerals have been extracted.
trackless mining	Underground transportation, loading and drilling of ore using rubber-tired vehicles, instead of the conventional locomotives and mine cars on narrow gauge tracks. In a stope or working face, a rubber-tired multiple drill carriage may replace a hand-held or post-mounted rock drill.
trench	A long, narrow excavation dug through overburden to bedrock, or blasted out of rock, to expose a vein or ore structure for examination and sampling.
tunnel	A horizontal underground passage that is open to the atmosphere at both ends; also applied loosely to an adit.
vein	A fissure, fault or crack in a rock filled by minerals that have travelled upwards from some deep source.
waste	Barren rock in a mine, or at least material that is too low in grade to be of economic value.
weathering	The chemical and mechanical breakdown of rocks and minerals under the action of atmospheric agencies. Eventually, most surface rocks crumble into soil.
wedge	As used in diamond drilling, refers to the placing of a wedge at some point in the hole, for the purpose of deflecting the bit in another direction.
winze	A vertical or inclined opening sunk from a point inside a mine. Similar to a shaft, but the latter starts at surface.
zone	An area or region which is distinct from the surrounding rock, either because of a difference in the type or structure of rocks, or because of mineralization.

DOME MINES LIMITED
WAGES, SUPPLIES, SERVICES AND TAXES PAID

Year	Wages, Salaries and Fringe Benefits	Supplies and Services	Federal Income Ontario Corporation and Mining Taxes
Totals prior to 1948	$32,465,000	$29,187,000	$16,064,000
1948	2,449,000	1,608,000	539,000
1949	2,565,000	1,644,000	384,000
1950	2,790,000	1,772,000	354,000
1951	3,189,000	1,598,000	434,000
1952	3,377,000	1,620,000	
1953	3,361,000	1,699,000	
1954	3,497,000	1,974,000	336,000
1955	3,709,000	2,070,000	261,000
1956	3,730,000	2,108,000	242,000
1957	3,962,000	2,477,000	243,000
1958	4,026,000	2,031,000	137,000
1959	4,034,000	2,073,000	250,000
1960	4,179,000	2,264,000	301,000
1961	4,127,000	2,016,000	416,000
1962	4,419,000	2,333,000	483,000
1963	4,382,000	2,215,000	620,000
1964	4,370,000	2,301,000	692,000
1965	4,642,000	2,463,000	539,000
1966	5,017,000	2,581,000	380,000
1967	5,416,000	2,462,000	456,000
1968	5,794,000	2,504,000	269,000
1969	5,793,000	2,824,000	123,000
1970	5,497,000	2,917,000	189,000
1971	5,466,000	2,931,000	69,000
1972	5,379,000	2,873,000	81,000
1973	6,291,000	4,085,000	2,869,000
1974	8,522,000	5,527,000	3,948,000
1975	10,170,000	5,703,000	2,228,000
1976	10,537,000	5,328,000	336,000
1977	10,094,000	5,794,000	836,000
1978	10,461,000	6,056,000	3,132,000
1979	12,039,000	6,868,000	8,029,000
1980	16,599,000	8,966,000	20,210,000
1981	16,754,000	9,957,000	3,990,000
TOTALS	**$239,102,000**	**$142,829,000**	**$69,440,000**

DOME MINES LIMITED

| Year | TOTAL ORE RESERVES AT YEAR END | | DRIFTS AND CROSSCUTS | FOOTAGE DIAMOND DRILLING | SHAFT SINKING |
	Tons	Ozs. per ton	Footage	Surface and Underground Excludes Blastholes	Footage
1911			1,310	10,079	105
1912	566,000	0.364	3,894	10,125	155
1913	512,600	0.233	4,416	1,672	223
1914	2,782,800	0.201	4,382	5,875	83
1915	2,600,000	0.300	7,095	5,654	877
1916	2,250,000	0.257	4,477	18,085	234
1917	3,500,000	0.259	4,588	10,066	178
1918	3,500,000	0.259	1,564	2,817	199
1919			2,638	2,151	
1920			4,005	13,769	
1921	Not		6,643	17,507	420
1922	Calculated		10,317	16,621	125
1923	from 1919		6,508	14,138	471
1924	to 1927	No Ore	10,826	21,271	237
1925		Reserve	12,431	38,940	684
1926		Grade	12,843	37,250	441
1927		Calculated	12,933	26,985	786
1928	1,250,000	From 1919	8,757	20,104	1,033
1929	1,300,000	to 1934	13,229	14,304	633
1930	1,900,000		5,718	14,641	779
1931	1,920,000		8,919	19,475	457
1932	2,000,000		9,696	26,950	501
1933	2,025,000		10,391	36,600	460
1934	2,000,000		9,843	33,461	640
1935	2,000,000	0.360	14,293	41,479	791
1936	2,250,000	0.383	15,749	42,147	859
1937	2,625,000	0.382	14,645	32,580	1,674
1938	2,620,000	0.365	12,830	22,309	235
1939	2,567,000	0.349	13,815	21,167	53
1940	2,600,000	0.339	13,821	25,870	31
1941	2,520,000	0.328	13,629	45,256	68
1942	2,430,000	0.316	13,439	26,869	42
1943	2,426,000	0.293	7,957	16,578	12
1944	2,353,000	0.278	6,430	11,731	
1945	2,412,000	0.271	8,800	48,650	
1946	2,498,000	0.261	14,438	62,503	
1947	2,508,000	0.260	16,279	67,312	
1948	2,447,000	0.252	19,295	53,159	
1949	2,496,000	0.253	20,315	71,442	
1950	2,479,000	0.252	17,867	77,522	
1951	2,448,000	0.255	18,927	92,627	
1952	2,472,000	0.259	18,649	88,171	
1953	2,470,000	0.263	18,622	100,576	
1954	2,461,000	0.262	18,603	98,282	
1955	2,498,000	0.257	16,821	95,154	
1956	2,475,000	0.256	14,753	106,016	
1957	2,472,000	0.257	15,836	96,996	
1958	2,479,000	0.256	14,689	87,055	
1959	2,494,000	0.261	14,954	97,173	
1960	2,476,000	0.259	15,050	98,568	
1961	2,455,000	0.258	15,004	97,811	
1962	2,426,000	0.257	15,818	103,882	975

DOME MINES LIMITED

| Year | TOTAL ORE RESERVES AT YEAR END | | DRIFTS AND CROSSCUTS | FOOTAGE DIAMOND DRILLING | SHAFT SINKING |
	Tons	Ozs. per ton	Footage	Surface and Underground Excludes Blastholes	Footage
1963	2,405,000	0.263	17,506	105,760	220
1964	2,350,000	0.267	20,519	111,364	
1965	2,285,000	0.267	20,430	115,211	148
1966	2,211,000	0.272	14,796	118,743	255
1967	2,028,000	0.279	14,095	96,329	
1968	1,926,000	0.280	14,112	87,758	
1969	1,819,000	0.271	7,286	79,626	
1970	1,685,000	0.282	3,516	89,904	
1971	1,473,000	0.276	4,377	91,165	
1972	1,590,000	0.267	3,017	60,032	
1973	1,691,000	0.255	3,421	79,676	
1974	1,871,000	0.241	6,376	86,176	
1975	1,933,000	0.226	4,213	68,263	
1976	1,890,000	0.227	2,376	55,097	
1977	1,867,000	0.221	1,697	37,943	
1978	1,859,000	0.221	4,082	43,030	
1979	1,896,000	0.216	3,595	37,637	
1980	2,149,455	0.206	5,676	61,785	
1981	2,146,716	0.207	8,422	36,965	95

Note from 1919 Annual Report
Ore Reserves

Experience with stoping and developing the orebodies in the Dome has demonstrated conclusively the futility of attempting to accurately estimate their tonnage and value in the conventional manner, on account of the irregularity of their form, and the extremely erratic distribution of gold in them. For the past seven years an earnest effort has been made to make these estimates and an immense amount of engineering data has been accumulated and worked up each year, but in the final analysis an intimate knowledge of the mine together with the figures for the past actual performance of ore bearing zones, and the condition of existing exposures of ore have to be more heavily drawn upon than the accurately assembled sampling and surveying data.

We feel, therefore, that a sounder forecast of the future life and earning power of the property can be given by not attempting to be specific in the matter of ore tonnage and value, but that we should confine ourselves to a broad statement based on a wide review of all the data available. We propose, therefore, to confine ourselves to stating that your property contains Ore Reserves at the present time sufficient to enable us to continue operating at the full capacity of your plant for a period of three to four years.

DOME MINES LIMITED
PRODUCTION RECORD

Year	Tons Milled	Production Value In Canadian Dollars	Recovery Per Ton Dollars	Recovery Per Ton Ounces Gold	Ounces (troy) Gold Recovered	Ounces (troy) Silver Recovered	Dividends Paid - Canadian Dollars	Operating Cost Per Ton Milled
1910	247	$ 4,355	$17.63	0.868	214.48	18.87		
1911		4,277			206.90			
1912	75,088	737,499	9.82	0.473	35,515.00	5,448.00		4.95
1913	131,149	1,242,625	9.47	0.457	59,912.00	7,076.00		4.19
1914	221,390	1,059,238	4.78	0.230	51,026.00	8,400.00		2.97
1915	317,740	1,530,286	4.82	0.232	73,725.94	12,389.78	400,000.00	2.56
1916	444,900	2,153,820	4.84	0.233	103,808.82	17,689.44	800,000.00	2.70
1917	359,570	1,480,174	4.12	0.198	71,193.42	10,658.66	300,000.00	2.78
1918	Clean Up	82,127			3,948.24	576.25		
1919	187,580	1,290,300	6.88	0.330	61,893.04	9,420.50		3.44
1920	295,220	2,243,926	7.60	0.329	97,022.88	14,779.55	419,166.75	4.53
1921	335,680	2,386,357	7.11	0.329	110,316.25	15,628.37	476,667.00	4.56
1922	368,400	4,178,936	11.34	0.546	201,124.47	29,249.72	715,000.50	5.26
1923	400,600	4,405,199	11.00	0.526	210,609.90	31,137.72	1,430,001.00	4.66
1924	493,400	4,307,624	8.73	0.420	207,277.23	33,666.12	1,906,668.00	4.58
1925	530,200	4,365,923	8.23	0.396	210,051.21	34,793.51	1,906,668.00	4.47
1926	555,700	3,940,053	7.09	0.341	189,631.62	32,772.58	1,906,668.00	4.17
1927	543,300	4,031,575	7.42	0.357	194,199.73	29,992.65	1,191,667.50	4.06
1928	548,000	3,915,051	7.14	0.344	188,626.41	27,347.82	953,334.00	3.85
1929	452,900	3,590,535	7.93	0.382	173,041.81	25,567.78	953,334.00	4.48
1930	67,600	774,943	11.46	0.553	37,415.90	3,958.68	953,334.00	4.12
1931	542,600	3,636,805	6.70	0.313	169,685.60	15,540.43	953,334.00	3.48
1932	536,450	4,581,131	8.54	0.364	195,110.70	28,580.52	1,239,334.20	3.88
1933	546,500	6,103,340	11.17	0.400	218,484.67	21,896.93	1,716,001.20	3.73
1934	547,600	7,177,086	13.10	0.376	206,157.67	18,938.68	3,336,669.00	3.88
1935	549,100	7,286,191	13.27	0.377	206,795.03	33,735.68	3,813,336.00	4.14
1936	553,900	7,315,168	13.21	0.376	208,528.22	24,835.73	3,873,336.00	4.49
1937	576,300	7,484,436	12.99	0.370	213,403.19	38,978.36	4,380,003.00	4.90
1938	601,700	7,293,289	12.12	0.344	206,956.76	28,650.90	3,893,336.00	4.26
1939	615,000	7,462,379	12.13	0.334	205,479.85	24,668.37	3,893,336.00	4.25
1940	621,600	7,933,786	12.76	0.331	205,583.88	35,210.38	3,893,336.00	4.21
1941	627,700	7,769,368	12.38	0.321	201,471.78	34,165.24	3,893,336.00	4.39
1942	559,700	6,579,536	11.76	0.305	170,546.76	34,668.65	3,309,335.60	4.57
1943	525,900	5,772,521	10.98	0.285	149,640.92	29,332.87	3,114,668.80	4.13
1944	519,800	5,177,495	9.96	0.258	134,230.06	24,960.21	2,920,002.00	4.28
1945	527,100	4,887,263	9.27	0.240	126,676.73	26,384.77	2,336,001.60	4.66
1946	573,400	5,448,935	9.50	0.257	147,649.25	34,543.06	2,287,334.90	5.24
1947	595,200	5,601,804	9.41	0.268	159,383.60	32,551.96	1,995,334.70	5.50
1948	620,800	5,463,596	8.80	0.250	155,470.41	29,762.06	1,654,667.80	6.25
1949	639,300	5,494,834	8.60	0.237	151,519.163	30,289.74	1,362,667.60	6.51
1950	680,000	6,097,497	8.97	0.235	159,903.60	29,856.99	1,411,334.30	6.69
1951	688,000	6,135,843	8.92	0.241	165,746.572	36,927.42	1,460,001.00	7.19
1952	687,400	5,803,685	8.44	0.246	168,794.692	26,925.77	1,362,667.60	7.63
1953	687,300	5,869,641	8.54	0.247	169,743.00	32,703.00	1,362,667.60	7.67
1954	697,600	5,867,430	8.41	0.246	171,399.00	34,604.00	1,362,667.60	7.66
1955	711,800	5,921,789	8.32	0.240	170,620.00	31,179.00	1,362,667.60	7.43
1956	709,600	5,876,186	8.28	0.240	170,013.00	32,131.00	1,362,667.60	7.42
1957	696,800	5,733,769	8.23	0.244	169,836.00	35,630.00	1,460,001.00	7.85
1958	707,900	5,962,970	8.42	0.247	174,701.00	37,418.00	1,362,667.60	7.96
1959	712,900	5,871,435	8.24	0.244	173,851.00	36,027.00	1,362,667.60	7.77
1960	714,600	6,025,370	8.43	0.247	176,338.151	38,412.48	1,362,667.60	7.96
1961	714,700	6,211,625	8.69	0.244	174,282.560	38,231.96	1,362,667.60	7.90

Year	Tons Milled	Production Value In Canadian Dollars	Recovery Per Ton Dollars	Ounces Gold	Ounces (troy) Gold Recovered	Ounces (troy) Silver Recovered	Dividends Paid - Canadian Dollars	Operating Cost Per Ton Milled
1962	714,500	6,482,499	9.07	0.241	172,118.255	38,346.32	1,362,667.60	8.43
1963	714,800	6,656,616	9.31	0.245	175,048.341	34,856.11	1,557,334.40	8.48
1964	714,500	6,760,881	9.46	0.249	177,593.623	40,083.67	1,557,334.40	8.62
1965	713,000	6,794,769	9.53	0.250	178,549.766	41,349.36	1,752,001.20	9.09
1966	712,500	6,805,509	9.55	0.251	178,987.567	40,321.19	1,752,001.20	9.90
1967	708,800	6,845,724	9.66	0.253	179,347.046	43,881.21	1,557,334.40	10.24
1968	712,900	6,911,444	9.69	0.253	180,668.438	41,477.96	1,557,334.40	10.81
1969	705,500	6,851,944	9.71	0.255	179,661.261	42,122.43	1,557,334.40	10.90
1970	690,400	6,664,437	9.65	0.262	180,585.718	38,485.38	1,557,334.40	10.77
1971	658,000	6,038,114	9.18	0.258	169,531.432	31,024.88	1,557,334.40	11.30
1972	629,800	8,840,722	14.04	0.232	146,242.451	23,421.02	1,557,334.40	11.71
1973	682,200	15,506,033	22.73	0.218	148,511.596	23,589.82	2,336,001.60	12.72
1974	701,600	19,579,898	27.91	0.173	121,032.482	20,209.14	4,088,002.80	16.74
1975	708,000	18,242,937	25.77	0.165	117,088.545	19,681.02	6,424,004.40	19.54
1976	708,300	14,613,166	20.63	0.169	119,503.787	20,749.98	5,496,003.60	19.74
1977	685,800	15,523,436	22.64	0.137	94,261.418	17,697.73	5,152,003.20	20.36
1978	679,200	21,782,071	32.07	0.139	94,160.668	22,562.54	6,440,004.00	25.17
1979	663,900	35,149,116	52.94	0.143	94,702.013	15,657.20	9,112,605.66	29.25
1980	678,100	62,577,732	92.28	0.127	85,893.624	13,467.94	13,089,304.35	35.65
1981	557,200	40,446,081	72.59	0.131	73,131.138	12,169.90	17,846,218.00	50.30
Total	**39,355,914**	**556,644,155**	**14.14**	**0.270**	**10,625,382.23**	**1,889,467.96**	**172,082,716.66**	

NOTES

The value of production is in Canadian funds and includes exchange premium on gold sold in the United States.

Dividends Paid are shown in Canadian Dollars, although prior to 1941 dividends were paid in U.S. funds.

Mill was closed from November 1917 to May 1919 due to shortage of labour caused by First World War.

There was no mill production in 1911 because of the destruction of the almost completed mill building by the Porcupine fire July 11, 1911.

Sigma Mines (Quebec) Limited
Statistics from Commencement of Operations
1937 to 1981

Ore Milled	Tons	18,725,127
Production Value	Can. $	260,853,876
Gold Recovered	Ozs. Troy	3,207,918
Silver Recovered	Ozs. Troy	625,985
Gold Recovered Grade	Ozs. per ton	0.1713
Dividends Paid	Can. $	29,485,000
Ore Reserves December 31, 1981		
Ore in Place	Tons	1,042,800
Average Grade	Ozs. per ton	0.197
Broken Ore	Tons	151,200

Campbell Red Lake Mines Limited
Statistics from Commencement of Operations
1947 to 1981

Ore Milled	Tons	8,352,516
Production Value	Can. $	624,071,353
Gold Recovered	Ozs. Troy	5,104,218
Silver Recovered	Ozs. Troy	397,261
Gold Recovered Grade	Ozs. per ton	0.611
Dividends Paid	Can. $	120,093,886
Ore Reserves December 31, 1981	Tons	2,315,900
Ore Reserve Grade December 31, 1981	Ozs. per ton	0.620

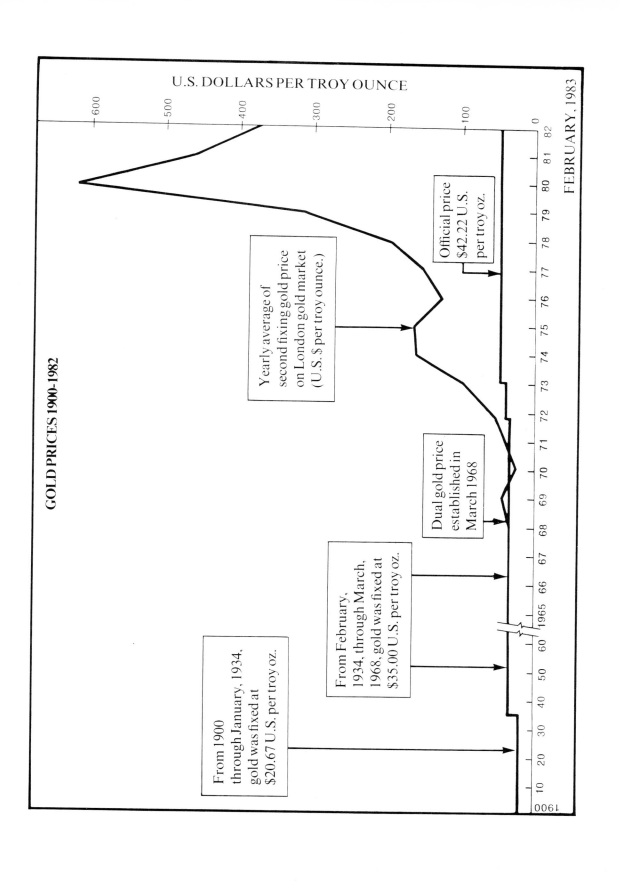

GOLD PRICES 1900-1982

U.S. DOLLARS PER TROY OUNCE

Yearly average of
second fixing gold price
on London gold market
(U.S. $ per troy ounce.)

Official price
$42.22 U.S.
per troy oz.

Dual gold price
established in
March 1968

From February,
1934, through March,
1968, gold was fixed at
$35.00 U.S. per troy oz.

From 1900
through January, 1934,
gold was fixed at
$20.67 U.S. per troy oz.

FEBRUARY, 1983

DOME MINES LIMITED
OFFICERS AND DIRECTORS

NAME	POSITION	YEARS SERVED
Adamson, G. Alexander	Director	1975 – 1977
Alexander, James E.	Assistant Secretary	1967 – 1973
	Assistant Secretary	1978 – 1980
Amyot, René	Director	1981 –
Allen, Innis, P.	Director	1925 – 1934
Andrecheck, Edmund J.	Assistant Treasurer	1970 – 1975
	Treasurer	1976
	Vice-President	1977
Ashley, James L.	Treasurer & Assistant Secretary	1912- 1914
Bache, Jules S.	Director	1918 – 1943
	President & Treasurer	1919 – 1942
	Chairman of the Board	1943
Baragwanath, J.G.	Director	1937 – 1942
Biggs, William R.	Director	1960 – 1974
Bostwick, W.A.	Vice-President	1912 – 1914
Brehaut, C. Henry	Vice-President Operations	1978 –
Bruce, G.S. Wallace	Vice-President Exploration	1972 –
Brunie, Henry C.	Director	1945 – 1966
Burnett, Frederick	Director	1932 – 1936
Butterman, H.H.	Assistant Secretary	1923 – 1943
Calvin, C.C.	Director	1944 – 1962
	Assistant Secretary	1923 – 1943
	Secretary	1944 – 1962
	Vice-President	1957 – 1962
Carson, James L.	Director	1949 – 1959
Converse, E.C.	Director	1912 – 1914
Corning, Frederick G.	Director	1922 – 1923
Curtis, Alfred H.	Director	1916 – 1921
	Assistant Secretary	1915 – 1922
de la Mar, J.R.	Director	1912 – 1918
	President & Treasurer	1915 – 1918
Denison, C.L.	Director	1912 – 1914
De Pencier, H.P.	Vice-President	1915 – 1934
	General Manager	1921 – 1934
Dowsett, C.W.	General Superintendent	1924 – 1926
Dye, Robert E.	General Superintendent	1935 – 1936
	Assistant General Manager	1937 – 1944
	General Manager	1945 – 1952
	Vice-President	1946 – 1953

NAME	POSITION	YEARS SERVED
Edwards, W.S.	Director	1910 – 1925
	President	1911
	Vice-President	1912 – 1923
Fasken, Alex	Director	1910 – 1943
	Secretary	1910 – 1943
	Vice-President	1941 – 1943
Fay, Brian C.	Director	1942 – 1959
Fell, Fraser M.	Director	1971 –
	Assistant Secretary	1963 – 1970
	Secretary	1971 – 1980
	Vice-Chairman of the Board	1981 –
Finucane, T.R.	Director	1919 – 1924
	Vice-President	1923 – 1924
Finucane, T.W.	Director	1923 – 1924
Gallagher, John P.	Director	1976 –
Girdwood, Charles P.	Director	1967 – 1975
	General Superintendent	1947 – 1952
	General Manager	1953 – 1972
	Vice-President	1963 – 1975
Goetz, E.P.	Assistant Secretary	1922 – 1952
Harris, G.H.	Director	1929 – 1941
Hick, John W.W.	Secretary	1981 –
Hough, John H.	Assistant Secretary	1971 – 1973
	Assistant Secretary	1978 –
Hoyt, Colgate	Director	1919 – 1921
Hutchison, Robert B.	Treasurer	1977 – 1980
James, William F.	Director	1957 –
Jamieson, T.N.	Director	1910 & 1915
	Treasurer	1911
Johns, William H.	General Superintendent	1945 – 1946
Jones, Maclean E.	Director	1978 –
Jordan, F.S.	Assistant Treasurer	1912 – 1914
Kaeding, C.D.	Director	1919 – 1921
	Vice-President & General Manager	1915 – 1920
Lambert, Allen T.	Director	1960 –
Lee, Dwight B.	Director	1923 – 1937
Loveys, George C.	Director & Secretary	1910
Macdonell, H.W.	Assistant Treasurer	1963 – 1969
MacKenzie, Bryce R.	Director	1963 – 1970
	Assistant Secretary	1952 – 1962
	Secretary	1963 – 1970

NAME	POSITION	YEARS SERVED
McCarthy, John F.H.	Director & President	1910
McCausland, John K.	Director	1975 – 1980
McCrae, Alex D.	Director	1938 – 1946
McCrea, J.G.	Vice-President	1946 – 1953
McFarland, Alan R.	Director	1981 –
Marsh, F.H.	Director	1944 – 1948
Matthews, A. Bruce	Director	1947 –
	Chairman of the Board	1976 –
Maulsen, Frank E.	Director	1930 – 1938
Meek, H.C.	General Superintendent	1912 – 1914
Michel, Clifford L.	Director	1976 – 1981
Michel, Clifford W.	Director	1939 – 1976
	Vice-President	1940 – 1941
	Vice President & Treasurer	1942
	President & Treasurer	1943 – 1958
	Chairman of the Board & Treasurer	1959 – 1976
Miller, George C.	Director	1915 – 1940
	Vice-President	1927 – 1940
Monell, Ambrose	Director	1911 – 1914
	Vice-President & General Manager	1911
	President	1912 – 1914
Nesbitt, Wallace	Director	1924 – 1929
Osler, Britton	Director	1910
Parker, James	Director	1910
Perry, Robert J.	General Superintendent	1972 –
Pershing, F. Warren	Director	1941 – 1980
Pighi, Adele C.	Assistant Secretary	1971 – 1973
Poillon, Howard	Director	1920 – 1922
Pomeroy, R.W.	Director	1915
	Director	1923 – 1928
Pyke, Harry V.	General Superintendent	1971
	Manager	1972 – 1982
	General Manager	1983 –
Quesnel, Robert R.	Controller	1981 –
Redpath, James B.	Director	1955 –
	Executive Vice-President	1954 – 1958
	President	1959 – 1977
Reynolds, J. Keith	Director	1981 –
Richards, William E.	Director	1978 –
Robinson, Arthur D.	General Superintendent	1954 – 1970

NAME	POSITION	YEARS SERVED
Robinson, John B.	Assistant Secretary	1922 – 1951
Scharf, H. Douglas	Controller	1978 – 1980
	Treasurer	1981 –
Sedgewick, George H.	Director	1911
Segsworth, R.F.	Director	1927 – 1932
Stein, Simon N.	Director	1935 – 1944
Stern, Morton F.	Director	1922 – 1923
	Director	1925 – 1954
	Vice-President	1922 – 1939
Stout, Andrew V.	Director	1916 – 1918
Stovel, Joseph H.	Director	1943 – 1956
	General Superintendent	1928 – 1934
	Vice-President	1935 – 1956
	General Manager	1935 – 1944
	Managing Director	1945 – 1951
Struthers, A.T.	Director	1910 – 1911
Taschereau, Malcolm A.	Director	1976 –
	Vice-President	1975 – 1977
	President & Chief Executive Officer	1978 –
Wexler, Sol	Assistant Treasurer	1919
Wilson, J.S.	Director	1910 – 1918
	Vice-President	1911
Wood, E.F.	Vice-President	1912 – 1914
Wright, Kenneth P.	Chief Metallurgist	1980 –

THE DOME MINES COMPANY LIMITED
(Incorporated under The Ontario Companies Act)

DATE	DOCUMENT	AUTHORIZED CAPITAL
March 23, 1910	Letters Patent	250,000 shares par value of $10.00 each $2,500,000
August 29, 1911	Supplementary Letters Patent (Increase in authorized capital) 100,000 shares with par value of $10.00 per share	350,000 shares par value of $10.00 each. $3,500,000
June 6, 1913	Supplementary Letters Patent (Increase in authorized capital) 150,000 shares with par value of $10.00 per share	500,000 shares par value of $10.00 each $5,000,000
March 17, 1922	Supplementary Letters Patent (Decreasing authorized capital) par value $10.00 to $9.00 per share	500,000 shares par value of $9.00 each $4,500,000

DOME MINES LIMITED
(Incorporated under the laws of Canada)

DATE	DOCUMENT	AUTHORIZED CAPITAL	ISSUED CAPITAL
July 7, 1923	Letters Patent	1,000,000 shares no par value	
June 20, 1938	Supplementary Letters Patent (2 for 1 stock split)	2,000,000 shares no par value	
May 13, 1974	Supplementary Letters Patent (3 for 1 stock split) plus increase in authorized capital to 10,000,000 shares	10,000,000 shares no par value	
June 8, 1979	Supplementary Letters Patent (3 for 1 stock split)	30,000,000 shares no par value	
May 5, 1980	Certificate of Continuance under Canada Business Corporations Act	Unlimited	19,398,002
May 22, 1981	Certificate of Amendment (4 for 1 stock split of issued capital)	Unlimited	77,592,248

SIGMA MINES LIMITED
(Incorporated under the laws of Canada)

DATE	DOCUMENT	AUTHORIZED CAPITAL
April 21, 1934	Letters Patent incorporated - Federal Charter	3,000,000 shares no par value
February 22, 1938	Certificate of Surrender of Charter	

SIGMA MINES (QUEBEC) LIMITED
(No Personal Liability)

DATE	DOCUMENT	AUTHORIZED CAPITAL
July 26, 1937	Letters Patent (incorporation) Quebec Charter	1,000,000 shares par value $1.00 each
Sept. 16, 1974	Certificate of Change of Name (By-law changing name, effective the date By-law published in Quebec Official Gazette)	

LES MINES SIGMA (QUÉBEC) LIMITÉE
(Libre de responsabilité personelle)

DATE	DOCUMENT	AUTHORIZED CAPITAL
May 7, 1979	Supplementary Letters Patent change from par value to no par value and 2 for 1 stock split	2,000,000 shares no par value
May 5, 1980	Supplementary Letters Patent 2 for 1 stock split then increase in authorized capital from 4,000,000 to 10,000,000	10,000,000 shares no par value

CAMPBELL RED LAKE MINES LIMITED
(Incorporated under the laws of Ontario)

DATE	DOCUMENT	AUTHORIZED CAPITAL
July 18, 1944	Letters Patent (Incorporation)	3,500,000 shares par value $1.00 each
Nov. 20, 1947	Supplementary Letters Patent (Increase in authorized capital)	3,750,000 shares par value $1.00 each
Feb. 6, 1950	Supplementary Letters Patent (Increase in authorized capital)	4,000,000 shares par value $1.00 each
May 10, 1974	Certificate of Amendment of Articles (2 for 1 stock split and change in par value to $.50 per share)	8,000,000 shares par value $0.50 each
May 18, 1979	Certificate of Amendment of Articles (2 for 1 stock split and change to no par value)	16,000,000 shares no par value
May 6, 1980	Certificate of Amendment of Articles (increase in authorized capital to 35,000,000)	35,000,000 shares no par value
May 22, 1981	Certificate of Amendment of Articles (3 for 1 share split)	105,000,000 shares no par value

LIST OF ILLUSTRATIONS

INDEX